PETER JON BARNETT, Dip.S.C., M.C.C.Ed., Adv.Dip.Ed., formerly Head of Technical Studies at Rickmansworth Grammar School, is now Head of the Middle School at Rickmansworth School. He lectures at West Dean College, West Sussex in jewellery and at Summer Schools. An experienced GCE and CSE examiner for numerous examination boards, he is currently assistant examiner for O-Level Design Technology with the University of London. Recently appointed Director of York Summer School.

D1610697

key facts

GCE O-Level Passbooks

BIOLOGY, R. J. Whitaker, B.Sc. and
J. M. Kelly, B.Sc., M.I.Biol.

CHEMISTRY, C. W. Lapham, M.Sc.

ECONOMICS, J. E. Waszek, B.Sc.(Econ.)

ENGLISH LANGUAGE, Robert L. Wilson,
M.A.

FRENCH, G. Butler, B.A.

GEOGRAPHY, R. Knowles, B.A.

HISTORY (Political and Constitutional,
1815-1939), L. James, B.A., M.Litt.

HISTORY (Social and Economic, 1815-1939),
M.C. James, B.A.

MODERN MATHEMATICS, A. J. Sly, B.A.

PHYSICS, B. P. Brindle, B.Sc.

GCE O-Level Passbook

Technical Drawing

P. Barnett, Dip.S.C., M.C.C.Ed., Adv.Dip.Ed.

Published by Charles Letts & Co Ltd
London, Edinburgh, München and New York

First published 1982 by Charles Letts & Co Ltd
Diary House, Borough Road, London SE1 1DW

1st edition, 1st impression. 3.82.1
© Charles Letts & Co Ltd
Made and printed by Charles Letts (Scotland) Ltd
ISBN 0 85097 433 X

Contents

Section IV Technical Drawing, 124

Introduction

This book is intended for those technical drawing students taking the examinations leading to the General Certificate of Education at Ordinary Level or the Certificate of Secondary Education.

It is hoped that the book will be an aid to students, helping them to re-inforce their knowledge and also their revision.

There are many larger and certainly more comprehensive textbooks on the subject, but I have tried to condense the relevant material and to provide all the basic information that a two-year course student is likely to need.

The topics are rather self-contained for ease of revision, and this is perhaps alien to the nature of the subject, which is all embracing and inter-mixed. Nevertheless, it allows the student to know exactly what he or she has covered in the syllabus.

A section has been included that contains a varied collection of Engineering Drawing data and this would be of extra use to those following an engineering course.

Finally, a large chapter has been devoted to typical examination questions, which will enable each student to gain valuable experience over the whole range of topics.

Acknowledgements

My thanks are due to Hilary Bailey for her hard work in typing the manuscript and for her general help and correction of my many errors; to the various examination boards for the use of material from past examination papers; and last but not least to all my students, both past and present, whose good humour and company have made this book worthwhile.

Dedication
To Winifred Gwendoline and Philip Henry Barnett, my parents,
by way of thanks.

Section I Technical Drawing
Chapter 1
Introduction to technical drawing

Drawing equipment

The old adage that 'the best is only good enough' certainly holds true in technical drawing. It is far better to have a few pieces of top quality equipment rather than a case full of 'gimmicky' and inaccurate instruments, half of which are never used! There is a wide selection on the market and the student is well advised to shop around.

A number of firms offer substantial discounts to educational establishments and this is obviously one way to obtain first-class material.

Instruments
Neatness and accuracy are essential in technical drawing and the greatest attention and care must be given to the drawing instruments themselves. The minimum requirement would be two compasses, a small spring-bow compass for circles of smaller radius and a larger 'open-leg' compass for the general work. Both compasses can be used for stepping off distances from a ruler, but greater accuracy is obtained with the use of dividers.

In the buying of any spring-bow compass, the central wheel type is very much the best. Beam compasses, large spring-bow compasses, extension units, etc., are all part of the draughtsman's equipment, but my advice is to wait until you have gained some experience in the subject. You are then in a much better position to buy sensibly.

Rulers
If accuracy is to stand any chance at all, then the unit of measurement, i.e., the ruler, must be as accurate as possible. Transparent rulers, made from perspex or acrylic, scratch resistant and unbreakable are very reasonably priced. The ruler should be clearly marked in metric units – decimetres, centimetres and millimetres.

A great many books, diagrams and working drawings are **still** measured in Imperial measurements and I would therefore recommend a ruler with inches, tenths and sixteenths as well.

Pencils

The range and type of pencil offered to the draughtsman is considerable. Basically we are concerned with perhaps three grades of pencil: 4H for construction lines, 2H for top lines and HB for lettering and dimensioning. Good quality pencils are not expensive. Clutch pencils, initially more expensive, last very much longer and have the added advantage of interchangeable leads. The latest advance in the drawing pencil is the fineline pencil. The leads are in clutch pencil form and are generally in diameters of 0.3 mm, 0.5 mm, 0.7 mm and 0.9 mm. These fineline clutch pencils give continuously even lines and need no sharpening. They can also be used with the new plastic leads which are used on tracing paper and on drafting film. Whichever pencils are used it is essential that they should be kept sharp. Poor drawings are often the result of 'lazy sharpeners'.

Erasers

A good quality eraser of soft rubber or plastic is an extremely useful item. The eraser should not damage the surface of the paper and if all erasing is done before lining-in, then previous errors will be difficult to detect.

Set-squares and protractors

Acrylic, vinyl or perspex set-squares and protractors are relatively inexpensive. Scratch resistant and unbreakable units are recommended. Set-squares should be of a generous size, at least 10" or 250 mm on one of the sides. Protractors are available in half round or complete circles. Set-squares can be of the adjustable type giving a variety of angles through 90°. They are also very useful when drawing parallel lines.

T-square

T-squares consist of a blade and a stock; they are made of wood, perspex, moulded plastic or a combination of these materials. The blade is either tapered on the lower edge or parallel. Wooden T-squares unless of high quality have a tendency to warp and wear, and therefore, perhaps for the student, an inexpensive moulded plastic one is best. It is important to remember that the T-square is used with the stock against the vertical edge of the drawing board. It should never be used from the top of the board to draw vertical lines. The T-square is being superseded by the parallel-motion ruler and by balanced drafting machines. This is certainly the case in the professional situation.

Drawing boards

Drawing boards are usually made either from natural timber or composite materials, such as plywood or chipboard. Solid wood boards are expensive as they have to be made from good even-grained timber. Allowance has to be made for the natural contraction and expansion of the timber in the form of inserts and back batterns. For the student therefore, composite boards are more than adequate. They are either sanded to a fine finish or faced with PVC or a similar type of material. In some boards a metal or solid wood strip is attached to the vertical edges to give greater accuracy and lasting qualities. Whichever board is used, the size most suitable is A2 (470 mm × 650 mm). It is advisable to have some means of elevating the board at an angle, rather than for it to be used flat.

Clips and tape

Paper is held in position on the drawing board by means of stainless steel or chrome plated clips or by masking-tape. Clear type 'sellotape' is not recommended as it tears the paper on removal. Students must never use drawing pins as after a few weeks the drawing board would be punctured by masses of small holes which could make the drawing of straight lines very difficult!

Paper

The draughtsman uses **Cartridge** paper in various grades and sizes. The most useful size being A2 (420 mm × 594 mm) with a weight of around 120 grams per square metre. The paper is also available in a variety of qualities and finishes much too numerous to mention here. It is worth pointing out that while the school student still works on Cartridge paper, commercially and industrially a vast amount of drawing is on drafting film (a plastic polyester) or on tracing paper. For this purpose plastic leads and drafting inks are used to give dense black lines. The translucent drawings are then reproduced by means of photocopying.

To maintain accuracy, the drawing instruments need to be well cared for and should be protected by being kept in an instrument box or small case. The box is best lined with foam to prevent the movement of the contents. It is possible to purchase specially lined cases made from high density plastic which give first-class protection against damage. The drawings themselves can be carried and kept flat and clean by means of special folders or plastic tubes at very little cost.

Lines and lettering

For school and examination purposes the student is required to work on Cartridge paper. Therefore, the type of line and lettering used must be suitable for this kind of work. Differences may occur in the commercial situation where drafting film and tracing paper may impose different demands. **The British Standards Institution** recommends a standard to be observed throughout all engineering practice and for general technical drawing the types of line and lettering in common use are shown on the page opposite. All lines should be uniformly black, dense and bold. Two thicknesses of line are recommended: a thin line and a thick line, which should be from two to three times thicker than the thin line.

General comments

All chain lines should start and finish with a long dash.

When centre lines indicate centre points, the centre should be the crossing of two long dashes.

Centre lines should extend only a short distance beyond the view unless required for dimensioning or for other purposes.

When there are two views the line should not extend across the space between the views.

Centre lines should not stop at another line of the drawing.

Arcs should join at tangent points.

If an angle is formed by chain lines, then the corners should meet at a long dash.

Dashed lines should start and end with dashes in contact with the lines from which they originate.

In lettering, clarity, style, spacing and size are important. Numerals, often read on their own, have to be especially clear. In general, capital letters are used and these with dimensioning should not be less than 3 mm tall, although I would suggest 5 mm as a much better standard. Notes and captions should be placed so that they are read from the bottom of the page, i.e., in the same direction as the title block. Underlining of notes and captions is not recommended. Lettering should be practised thoroughly as often as possible, until it can be done naturally. Neatness of printing earns extra marks in most examinations, while indifferent printing often means loss of marks. Lettering as shown is used on drawings because it is easier to read than handwriting. Sloping letters and figures are acceptable though it is as well to develop one's lettering in the vertical style.

Types of Line

LINE	DESCRIPTION	APPLICATION
―――――	thick, continuous	Visible outlines and edges
―――――	thin, continuous	Dimensions, Lead lines, Projection lines, Cross-hatching
 ∿∿∿∿∿	thin, continuous irregular	Limits of partial views, boundary lines, short break lines
– – – – –	thin, short dashes	Hidden outlines and edges, portions to be removed
— – — – —	thin chain long	Centre lines
— · — · —	thin chain short	False views Adjacent parts
▬ – — – ▬	Chain, thick at ends and change of direction, thin elsewhere	Cutting planes or viewing planes
 ―√―√―√―	Ruled line and short zig-zag	Long break lines

Lettering and numerals

A B C D E F G H I J K L M N O P Q R S T U V W X Y Z

1 2 3 4 5 6 7 8 9 0

Figure 1

13

Dimensioning

Dimensioning is an important part of technical drawing. Numerous methods have been used, but the most up-to-date standards are shown opposite and are in line with the I.S.O. recommendations.

The distance between any two lines is shown by an **unbroken** line ending in arrow-heads. The arrow-heads should be neat and precise and go right up to the **lead lines** which extend from the drawing.

The dimension line should be at least 10 mm away from the view and the numerals either **above** the line, in the case of horizontal dimension lines, or to the **left** in the case of vertical ones.

All dimensions are in mm unless stated otherwise. The diameter ($\emptyset$) is always quoted for circles and the radius (R) is always used for arcs. Square sectioned material has the symbol $\square$. In all cases the symbol precedes the dimension. Angular dimensions should be expressed in degrees and minutes.

Large dimensions should be placed outside smaller dimensions. Dimensions that are not drawn to scale should be underlined. If at all possible, dimensions should be placed on the outside of any view and not on it.

Numerals should be placed so that they can be read from the bottom or from the right of the drawing.

Key terms

British Standards Institution   The body responsible for B.S. 308 'Engineering Drawing Practice'.
I.S.O.   International Organization for Standardization for Metric Drawings.
Lead lines   Thin, fine lines that project from the view and give an indication of width, height, length, etc., for dimensioning purposes.

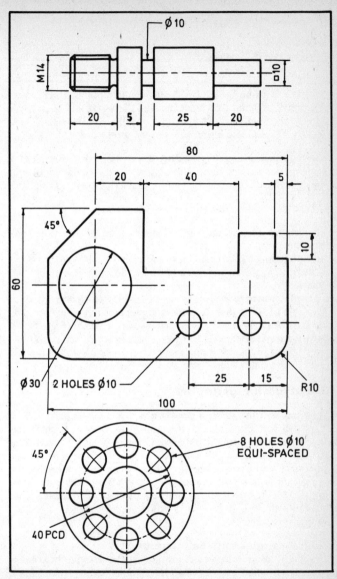

Figure 2

Section II Plane Geometry
Chapter 2
Lines and angles

An angle is formed when two lines meet at a point. Where these two **arms,** *AB* and *BC,* meet is called the **vertex** (Fig. 3a). We refer to the angle as *ABC* or *CBA,* usually with the sign $\angle ABC$ or $\widehat{ABC}$. The middle letter refers to the **vertex.**

The angle measurement is the **degree,** written °, for example 60°. A complete circle contains 360°. If the circle is divided into four equal parts, each corner is 90° and is called a **right-angle** (Fig. 3b).

Some other angles are also given special names.

An **obtuse** angle is an angle of **more** than 90° but **less** than 180° (Fig. 3c).
An **acute** angle is an angle of **less** than 90° (Fig. 3d).
A **reflex** angle is one greater than 180° but less than 360° (Fig. 3e).
Complementary angles are any two angles which add up to 90°. An angle of 30° is therefore the complement to an angle of 60°; an angle of 15° is the complement to an angle of 75° (Fig. 3f).
Supplementary angles are any two angles which add up to 180°. An angle of 65° is the supplement to an angle of 115°. An angle of 30° is the supplement to an angle of 150° (Fig. 3g).

Construction of angles

To draw angles with a protractor
A protractor, either semi-circular or completely circular has degrees marked around its circumference in unit °'s and tens of units °'s. However, this method of measuring degrees can be inaccurate and perhaps greater accuracy can be obtained by the use of set squares or compasses. It is also possible to draw angles with the use of an adjustable set-square. The great advantage with these is that once the angle is set it can be fixed for further reference.

To draw angles with set-squares
Using a T-square or parallel-motion on the drawing board it is possible to make use of set-squares to achieve certain angles, for example in Fig. 3h.

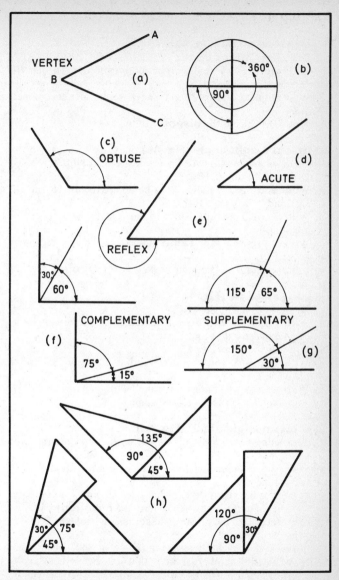

Figure 3

17

Making use of compasses to obtain angles

To bisect an angle (Fig. 4a)
(a) Draw lines AB and BC.
(b) With centre B and radius R scribe arcs to cut AB and BC at X and Y.
(c) With radius S and centres X and Y scribe arcs to intersect at D.
(d) Join BD, which is the **bisector** of the angle.

To trisect a right-angle (Fig. 4b)
Bisect means to cut into two. Trisect means to cut into three.
(a) Draw a right-angle ABC.
(b) With centre B and radius R scribe an arc to cut AB and BC at X and Y.
(c) With centre Y and the **same** radius R scribe an intersecting arc at D.
(d) With centre X and the **same** radius R scribe an intersecting arc at E.
(e) Join BD and BE. The right-angle is now **trisected.**

To copy an angle (Fig. 4c)
(a) Draw the given angle ABC.
(b) With centre B and a suitable radius R scribe an arc to cut AB and BC at X and Y.
(c) Draw the horizontal line ST.
(d) With centre S and the same radius R scribe an arc to cut ST at P.
(e) With centre P and radius YX from the original angle mark Q.
(f) Join S to Q. QST is the copied angle.

To draw an angle of 60° (Fig. 4d)
(a) Set compasses to any suitable radius R. Draw a circle with this radius.
(b) With the same radius R set off positions around the circumference.
(c) Note that the circumference has been divided into six equal sections (a useful fact when requiring a **hexagon**).
(d) Each section to the centre C makes an angle of 60°.

If we know that each circle has an angle of 360°, then it can be seen that the number of sides that any figure has (in this case six), divided into 360°, will give the angle at the centre. $360° \div 6 = 60°$.

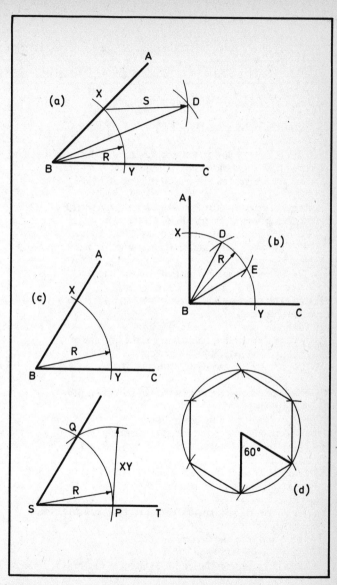

Figure 4

To draw an angle of 90° (Fig. 5a)
(a) Draw line AB.
(b) With centre C and suitable radius R draw a semi-circle to cut AB at X and Y.
(c) With centre X and Y and radius S scribe intersecting arcs at D.
(d) Join CD. DCA or DCB are right-angles.

To bisect any line AB (Fig. 5b)
(a) Draw line AB.
(b) With centres A and B and a radius greater than $\frac{1}{2}AB$, scribe arcs above and below AB, to intersect at D and E.
(c) Join DE: this is the bisector of the line AB.

To draw a perpendicular from a given point P outside a given straight line AB (Fig. 5c)
(a) From P scribe a suitable arc to cut AB at X and Y.
(b) With centre X, and centre Y and using the same radii, draw intersecting arcs at Q.
(c) Join PQ, which is perpendicular to the line AB.

To draw the perpendicular from a point P on a given line AB (Fig. 5d)
(a) With any point C outside the line, as centre, draw a circle passing through the point P to cut the line AB at Q.
(b) Join QC and extend to the circle at R.
(c) Join PR which is now perpendicular to the line AB.

To draw the fourth proportional to three given lines (Fig. 6a)
(a) Let A, B and C be the given lines.
(b) Draw two lines PQ and PR at an **acute** angle.
(c) Mark on these lines the lengths A, B and C as shown at S, T and X.
(d) Join ST. From X draw a line parallel to ST to cut PQ at Y.
(e) TY is the fourth proportional.

To draw the third proportional to two given lines (Fig. 6b)
(a) Let A and B be the two given lines.
(b) Draw two lines PQ and PR.
(c) Mark on these lines the lengths A and B as shown at S, T and X.
(d) Join ST. From X draw a parallel line to cut PQ at Y.
(e) PY is the third proportional.

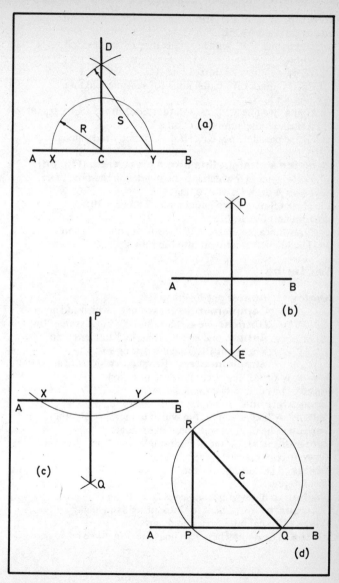

Figure 5

To divide a straight line into a given number of equal parts (Fig. 6c)

(a) Draw line *AB*, which is the line to be divided, into say 5 units.
(b) From *AB* draw an **acute** line *AC*.
(c) On *AC* mark off 5 equal units (of sensible lengths).
(d) Join *C5* to *B*.
(e) Using the line *C5B* as a datum line, draw lines parallel to it through the points 4, 3, 2 and 1.
(f) These parallel lines cut *AB* into the required equal parts.

To divide a straight line into a given ratio (Fig. 6d)

(a) Draw a line *AB* which is to be divided in the ratio 2:3:5.
(b) From *A* draw an **acute** line *AC*.
(c) Mark off on *AC* ten equal units (2+3+5 = 10).
(d) Join unit *C10* to *B*.
(e) Draw lines parallel to *C10B* through points *C2* and *C5*.
(f) The line *AB* is now cut into the ratio 2, 3 and 5.

Key terms

Angles   **Acute:** one less than 90°.
Complementary: two angles which add up to 90°.
Obtuse: one greater than 90° but less than 180°.
Reflex: one greater than 180° but less than 360°.
Right-angle: one measuring 90°.
Supplementary: two angles which add up to 180°.

Arc   Any part of the circumference of a circle.
Bisect   To cut into two equal parts.
Circumference   The outer edge containing a circle.
Datum   A line or angle from which to measure all others.
Degree   The unit measurement of an angle.
Perpendicular   A line at right-angles to a horizontal line.
Protractor   Instrument for measuring angles.
Radius   The distance from the centre of a circle to its circumference.
Scribe   To draw with compasses.
Set-square   Instrument for measuring fixed angles.
Trisect   To cut into three equal parts.
Vertex   The point where two lines meet to make an angle.

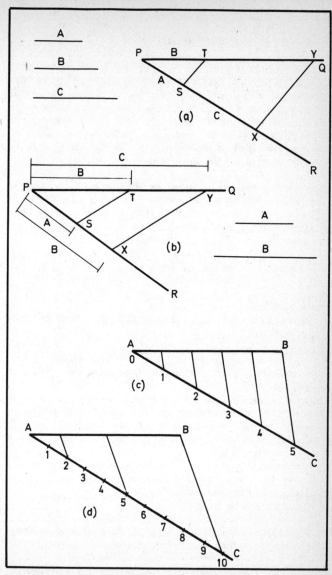

Figure 6

Chapter 3
Scales, plain and diagonal

It is not always possible to draw an object at its actual size. It therefore becomes necessary to reduce or increase, by **ratio,** its real size into a convenient one for the drawing board. If the object is easy to draw, then it is often simply a case of working out each dimension as it is needed and scaling up or down by calculation. However, in some cases it is quicker to use a **scale ruler** or to construct a scale for the purpose of reducing or enlarging the dimensions.

Scales are of two types: **plain or diagonal.** Each of these scales can be **full size, reduced** or **enlarged** scale. The scale must be clearly stated at the bottom of each drawing. The description of the scale can be expressed in a variety of ways. For example:

Scale	Half-full size
Scale	100 m to 200 m
Scale	50%
Scale	1:2

Plain scales
A plain scale is used when a **limited** number of sub-divisions is required.

Figure 7a shows a plain scale 20 mm to 1 m to read up to 4 m. When drawing this scale it is important to observe the following points:
1. The 0 on the scale is placed one unit (of the measure being used) in from the left. In this case that would be 20 mm. Each 20 mm on the scale represents 1 m on the **real** object. As we wish to read up to 4 m, three more divisions each of 20 mm are added from the 0 to the right.
2. The single division to the left of the 0 can now be sub-divided into convenient measurements. In this example we have four sub-divisions, each **representing** 25 cm.
3. The scale must be accurate.
4. The scale must be named, either as a ratio or as a percentage.
5. The height of the scale does not affect the horizontal divisions. This applies to both plain and diagonal scales.

Figures 7b and 7c show further examples on which **representative** measurements have been shown.

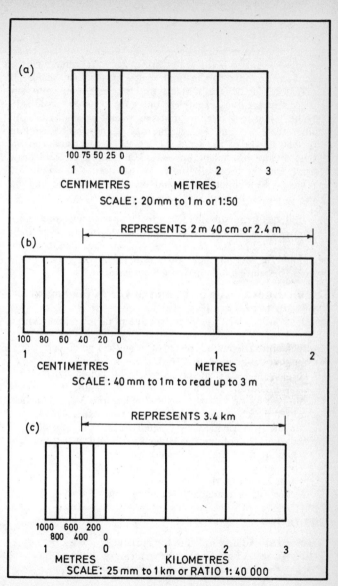

(a)

100 75 50 25 0
1   0   1   2   3
CENTIMETRES   METRES
SCALE : 20 mm to 1 m or 1:50

REPRESENTS 2 m 40 cm or 2.4 m

(b)

100 80 60 40 20 0
1   0   1   2
CENTIMETRES   METRES
SCALE : 40 mm to 1 m to read up to 3 m

REPRESENTS 3.4 km

(c)

1000 600 200
800 400 0
1   0   1   2   3
METRES   KILOMETRES
SCALE: 25 mm to 1 km or RATIO 1: 40 000

Figure 7

Diagonal scales

Diagonal scales are used where much smaller measurements are needed. They take longer to construct. Greater accuracy and care must be taken if the scales are to be worthwhile. All the same factors apply to diagonal scales as to plain scales. If we wish to divide the unit to the left of 0, not into say 4 or 5 as in previous examples, but into 20 or even 100 sub-divisions, then it is obvious that this would be impossible on a plain scale. In Fig. 8a, a unit has been sub-divided into four. The height of the scale AB can be any sensible height. Let us divide this height into say 5 as in Fig. 8b and draw vertical lines at those divisions. Please note that when any line has to be divided into equal divisions, then the method of Fig. 6c should be used.

The unit has been sub-divided into 20 spaces. Diagonal lines are drawn from the base to the top of each column, from right to left as in Fig. 8c. In Fig. 8d it can be seen how the movement in measurement progresses from diagonal line to diagonal line until a full unit has been measured.

To construct a scale of 40 mm to 1 m to read up to 3 m in units of 4 cm (Fig. 8e)

(a) Draw a line AB 120 mm in length and divide equally into 3 (3×40 mm).
(b) Each unit of 40 mm represents 1 m on the real object.
(c) Number the divisions 1, 0, 1, 2.
(d) The diagonal scale can have any sensible height AB.
(e) Draw in the vertical lines from 0, 1, 2 to the line B.
(f) The unit to the left of 0 is sub-divided into 5 equal vertical units and each of these sub-units **represents** 20 cm.
(g) The line AB is divided into 5 equal horizontal units.
(h) Each vertical column has a diagonal line drawn from right to left and from base to top as shown.
(i) Where each diagonal unit cuts a horizontal line a movement of 4 cm is measured.
(j) On the scale, a reading of 2 m and 32 cm is shown.

Key terms

Horizontal A line parallel to the horizon.
Percentage A figure expressed in terms of 100, e.g., 50%.
Scale ruler A manufactured ruler that is scaled to a fixed ratio, e.g., half-size or one-fifth size.
Vertical A line at right-angles to the horizon.

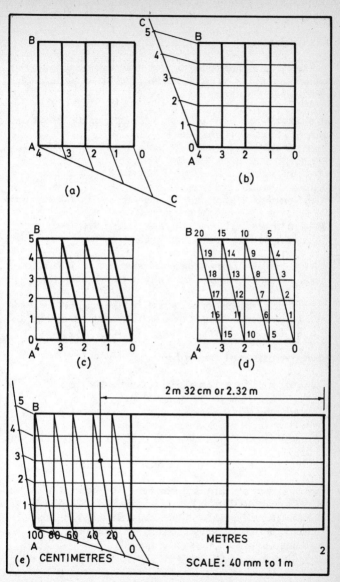

Figure 8

27

Chapter 4
Triangles

A triangle is a three-sided figure which can be classified by the lengths of its sides or by the size of its angles. Each corner is called a vertex (plural, vertices).

Equilateral All three sides are the same length, which also makes all three angles the same size (Fig. 9a).
Isosceles Has two sides the same length; the two angles opposite these sides are also equal (Fig. 9b).
Scalene All three sides are of different length and all three angles are also unequal (Fig. 9c).
Right-angled Has one angle a right-angle. The side opposite the right-angle is called the hypotenuse (Fig. 9d).
Obtuse angled Has one obtuse angle (Fig. 9e).
Acute angled Has three acute angles (Fig. 9f).

The three angles of **any** triangle add up to 180°, and therefore, if two angles are known the third can easily be calculated (Fig. 9g).

Any side of a triangle can be its base, but the height of a triangle is the perpendicular distance from its base to the vertex (Fig. 9h). This height is also referred to as the altitude.

Construction of triangles

To construct a triangle given three sides (Fig. 9i)
(a) Let *AB*, *AC* and *BC* be the given sides.
(b) Mark off *AB* as the base using compasses or dividers.
(c) With centre *A* and radius *AC* scribe an arc.
(d) With centre *B* and radius *BC* scribe an arc to cut the first at *C*.
(e) Join *AC* and *BC*. *ABC* is the required triangle.

To construct a triangle given two sides and the included angle (Fig. 9j)
(a) Let *AB*, *AC* be the given sides and *ABC* the given angle.
(b) Mark off *AB* as base using compasses or dividers.
(c) Using a protractor mark out angle *ABC*.
(d) With centre *A* and radius *AC* scribe an arc to cut the line from *B* at *C*.
(e) Join *AC*. *ABC* is the required triangle.

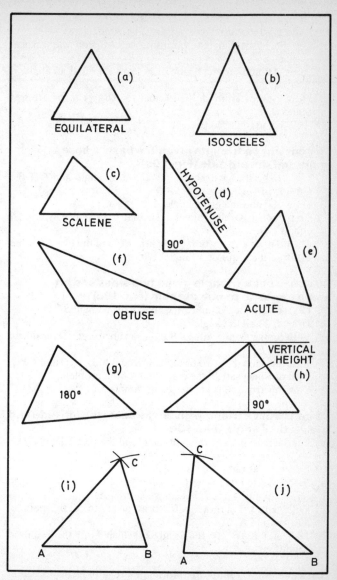

EQUILATERAL (a)

ISOSCELES (b)

SCALENE (c)

HYPOTENUSE (d)
90°

ACUTE (e)

OBTUSE (f)

180° (g)

VERTICAL HEIGHT (h)
90°

(i) C
A B

(j) C
A B

Figure 9

To construct an isosceles triangle given the altitude and the vertical angle (Fig. 10a)

(a) Let the vertical height (altitude) be AB and the vertical angle 60°.
(b) Draw AB and on **each** side draw arms set off at an angle of 30° (half 60°).
(c) From B draw a line perpendicular to AB to cut the arms at C and D.
(d) ACD is the required triangle.

To construct a triangle given the base, a base angle and the altitude (Fig. 10b)

(a) Let AB be the given base, 60° the base angle and CD the altitude or vertical height.
(b) Draw AB and the given angle ABC (60°).
(c) Construct a parallel line EF so that its distance from AB equals CD.
(d) The point of intersection of the arm BC and the line EF is the **apex** of the required triangle ABC.

To construct a triangle given two sides and an angle opposite to one of them (Fig. 10c)

(a) Let the sides be AB and BC and the given angle BCD.
(b) Draw BC and the angle BCD.
(c) With centre B and radius AB scribe an arc to cut CD produced at A and E.
(d) It can be seen that two triangles are possible, ABC and EBC, both of which satisfy the conditions of the problem.
(e) This construction is known as the 'ambiguous case'.

To construct a triangle given the base, the altitude and the vertical angle (Fig. 10d)

(a) Let the base be AB, the altitude C and the vertical angle D.
(b) At A construct angle BAF equal to D.
(c) Draw AG at right-angles to AF.
(d) Bisect AB to intersect AG at H.
(e) Draw a parallel line XY distance C from AB.
(f) With centre H and radius HA draw an arc to cut this parallel line in J and K.
(g) JAB and KAB are the triangles which fulfil the required conditions.

Note See Fig. 13f for more information regarding angles within a circle.

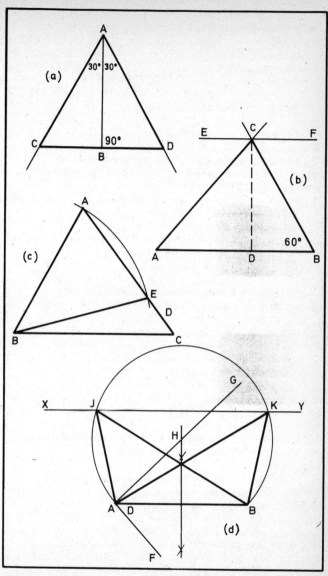

Figure 10

31

**To construct a triangle given the base, one of
the base angles and the sum of the other two sides
(Fig. 11a)**

(a) Let *AB* be the given base, *C* the given angle and *S* the
sum of the two sides.
(b) At *A*, produce the given angle *C* to form *BAE*.
(c) Make *AE* equal in length to the sum of the two sides (*S*).
(d) Join *EB* and bisect to cut *AE* at *G*.
(e) Join *GB*.
(f) *AGB* is the required triangle.

**To construct a triangle given the base, one of
the base angles and the difference of the other
two sides (Fig. 11b)**

(a) Let *AB* be the given base, *C* the given angle and *D* the
difference of the other two sides.
(b) At *A*, produce the given angle *C* to form *BAF*.
(c) Make *AE* equal to the difference of the other two sides (*D*).
(d) Join *EB* and bisect to cut *AF* produced at *G*.
(e) *AGB* is the required triangle.

**To construct a triangle with a given base and
having its angles in a given ratio (Fig. 11c)**

(a) Let *AB* be the given base and the ratio 2:3:4.
(b) Draw *AB* and describe a semi-circle at *A* (or *B*).
(c) Divide the circumference of the semi-circle into the total
number of the ratio parts, in this case 9.
(d) Draw lines through points 2 and 5 from *A*.
(e) From *B* draw a line parallel to *A*5.
(f) Produce *A*2 to cut this line from *B* at *D*.
(g) *ADB* is the required triangle.

**To construct a triangle given the base, the altitude
and the ratio of the two other sides
(Fig. 11d)**

(a) Let *AB* be the base, *C* the altitude and the ratio 2:3.
(b) Draw *AB* and the line *PQ* parallel and at a distance of *C* apart.
(c) Divide *AB* into 5 equal units (2 + 3).
(d) Mark point *D* so that *DB*:*DA* is 2:3.
(e) Extend *AB* to *E* so that *BE* is twice *AB*.
(f) Point *E* is so placed that *EB*:*EA* is 10:15 or 2:3.
(g) Bisect *DE* in *F*. With *F* as centre scribe an arc to cut
PQ in *G* and *H*.
(h) *AGB* or *AHB* are the required triangles.

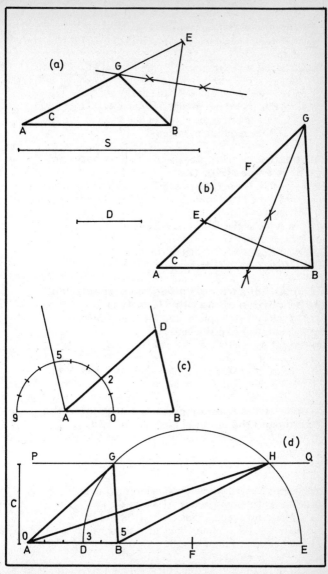

Figure 11

To construct a triangle given the perimeter, the altitude and one base angle (Fig. 12a)

(a) Let the base angle be 60°, the perimeter AB and the altitude C.
(b) Draw AB and the line PQ parallel and at a distance of C apart.
(c) From A make the angle 60° to cut PQ at D.
(d) On AB mark off AE so that BE equal AD.
(e) Join DE and bisect to cut AB in G.
(f) AGD is the required triangle.

To construct a triangle given the perimeter and the base angles (Fig. 12b)

(a) Let AB be the perimeter and C and D the base angles.
(b) Draw out AB and from A and B lay out the angles C and D to intersect at E.
(c) Bisect the angles EAB and EBA to meet at F.
(d) From F draw FG parallel to AE.
(e) From F draw FH parallel to BE.
(f) FGH is the required triangle.

To construct a triangle given the perimeter and the proportion of the sides (Fig. 12c)

(a) Let AB be the perimeter and the sides 4:5:6.
(b) Lay out AB and divide into 15.
(c) Set out $AC:CD:DB$ in the ratio of 4:5:6.
(d) With centre C and radius CA scribe an arc AE.
(e) With centre D and radius DB intersect the arc at E.
(f) CDE is the required triangle.

To construct a triangle given the perimeter, the altitude and the vertical angle (Fig. 12d)

(a) Let AB be **half** the perimeter, C the altitude and D the angle.
(b) Draw DE and DF equal in length to AB and enclosing angle D.
(c) From E and F draw perpendiculars to meet at G.
(d) With centre G and radius GE scribe the arc EF.
(e) With centre D and radius C scribe the arc PQ.
(f) Draw KL, the common tangent to these two arcs.
(g) DKL is the required triangle.

Note Information concerning the common tangent can be found in Fig. 21.

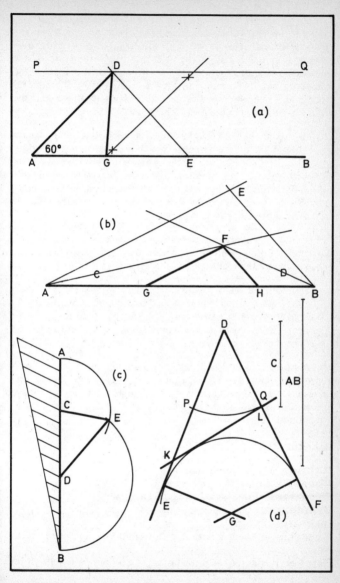

Figure 12

35

The right-angled triangle

There are several very useful facts to be observed concerning the right-angled triangle. If we take any right-angled triangle as in Fig. 13a, the areas of the squares drawn on each of the sides have a certain relationship. In any such triangle, the square on side A is equal in area to the sum of the squares $B + C$. The longest side A is called the **hypotenuse** and the theory is known as Pythagoras' Theorem.

It is also true that any circles constructed in a similar fashion upon the sides of the triangle will have the same equation. In Fig. 13b the area of circle A is equal to the areas of circles $B + C$. In both situations the areas of any of the figures can be obtained by either addition or subtraction. For example, area B can be obtained by subtracting area C from area A, area C by subtracting B from A.

In Fig. 13c the square $ACEF$ is twice the area of square $ABCD$. All triangles in a semi-circle, with the diameter as base AB, contain a right-angle at the circumference (Fig. 13d).

The right-angled triangle can be used in working out square-roots. In Fig. 13e the hypotenuse AC is equal in length to the square root of 5. $AB^2 + BC^2 = AC^2$ $(4 + 1 = 5)$. If another triangle is drawn on AC with $CD = 1$ unit, then AD is equal to the square root of 6.

Note Another useful fact is that any number of triangles with a common base AB within a circle, Fig. 13f, will contain the same angle at the circumference. The angle from the same base AB to the centre of the circle will be exactly **twice** that at the circumference.

Key terms

Altitude The vertical height of a triangle.
Apex The corner of a triangle opposite to its base.
Equilateral Equal sided and equal angled triangle.
Hypotenuse The side opposite the right-angle in a right-angled triangle.
Isosceles A triangle with two sides and their opposite angles equal.
Parallel A line equal in distance, for its entire length, from another line.
Scalene A triangle unequal on all sides and all angles.

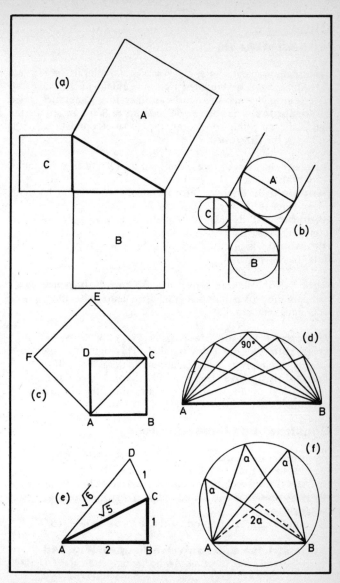

Figure 13

37

Chapter 5
Quadrilaterals

Quadrilateral means four sides and quadrilaterals are figures that are formed or bounded by four straight lines. They also have four angles and the figures are therefore sometimes called **quadrangles.** The four angles add up to 360°. In any of the figures the line joining one corner (vertex) to its opposite corner is known as the **diagonal.**

Square All its sides are equal and all its angles right-angles (Fig. 14a).
Rectangle Its opposite sides are equal and all the angles right-angles (Fig. 14b).
Rhombus All its sides are equal but its angles are not right-angles (Fig. 14c).
Rhomboid Its opposite sides are equal but its angles are not right-angles (Fig. 14d).

Note All the figures above are also **parallelograms** since the definition of a parallelogram is a figure with its opposite sides equal and parallel.

Trapezium Has two sides parallel (Fig. 14e).
Trapezoid Has no sides parallel. This figure is sometimes referred to simply as an irregular quadrilateral (Fig. 14f).
Trapezion or kite Has pairs of adjacent sides equal and is symmetrical about an axis or centre line. Its diagonal is at right-angles to the axis (Fig. 14g).

Construction of quadrilaterals

To construct a square on a given line (Fig. 14h)
(a) Let AB be the given line.
(b) At A draw the perpendicular $AC = AB$ (see Fig. 5).
(c) With centres B and C and radius AB scribe arcs to intersect at D.
(d) Join CD and BD to produce the required square $ABDC$.

To construct a square given a diagonal (Fig. 14i)
(a) Bisect the given diagonal AB by the perpendicular CD at O.
(b) With centre O describe the circle to touch $ADBC$.
(c) $ADBC$ is the required square.

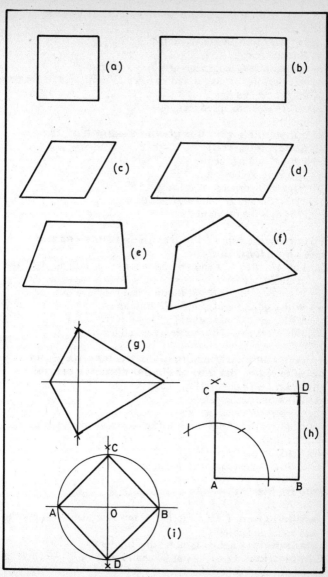

Figure 14

To construct a rectangle given the diagonal and one side (Fig. 15a)

(a) Let *AB* be the diagonal and *CD* the side.
(b) Bisect *AB* at *O*.
(c) With centre *O* and radius *OA* describe a circle.
(d) With centres *A* and *B* and radius *CD* draw arcs to cut the circle at *E* and *F*.
(e) *AEBF* is the required rectangle.

To construct a rhombus given the length of its diagonals (Fig. 15b)

(a) Let *AC* and *BD* be the given diagonals.
(b) Draw *AC* and bisect it at *E*.
(c) Draw *BD* perpendicular to *AC* at *E*.
(d) Make *EB* and *ED* equal to half *BD*.
(e) *ABCD* is the required rhombus.

To construct a quadrilateral given four sides and one angle (Fig. 15c)

(a) Let *AB*, *BC*, *CD* and *DA* be the given sides and *ABC* the given angle.
(b) Draw two sides *AB* and *BC* and the given angle.
(c) With centre *A* and radius *AD* draw an arc.
(d) With centre *C* and radius *CD* draw an arc.
(e) Join *AD* and *DC* to give the required figure.

To construct a trapezium given the lengths of the parallel sides, the perpendicular distance between them and one angle (Fig. 15d)

(a) Draw one of the parallels *AB*.
(b) Construct the parallel line *XY*.
(c) Construct the known angle from *A* to intersect the parallel line in *D*.
(d) Mark off the known length *DC*.
(e) *ABCD* is the required trapezium.

Key terms

Parallelogram General term for any figure with its opposite sides equal and parallel.
Quadrangle Another term for quadrilateral.
Symmetrical Equal about a centre line, e.g., a circle is symmetrical about its diameter.

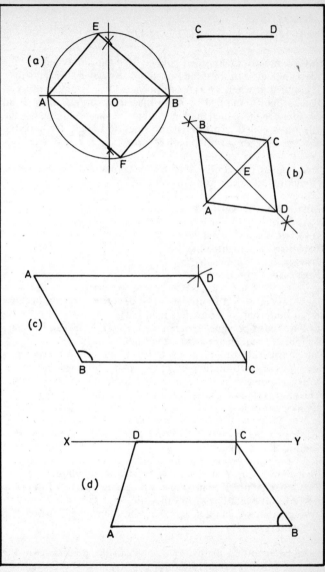

Figure 15

41

Chapter 6
Polygons

Polygon means 'many-sided' and so by definition could include any plane figure of three sides or more. However, it is generally accepted that when we refer to polygons it is in the context of a plane figure bounded by more than four straight lines. If all the sides are the same length and all the angles are the same, the polygon is called **regular.** If the sides and angles are not the same the polygon is said to be **irregular.**

Each regular polygon is given a specific name depending upon the number of sides it contains.

Pentagon   five-sided
Hexagon   six-sided
Heptagon   seven-sided
Octagon   eight-sided
Nonagon   nine-sided
Decagon   ten-sided

These regular polygons are said to be **convex** polygons because all their internal angles are less than 180°.
A **re-entrant** polygon has a hollow shape (Fig. 16f) and has one or more internal angles greater than 180°.
The **diagonal** of a polygon is a line drawn across the polygon from one corner to another, except when the corners are adjacent. A regular polygon may be constructed upon a given line or within a given circle and use is often made of this fact when constructing polygons.

The three most commonly used polygons are shown in Figs. 16a, b and c. The angles of any regular polygon can be determined by dividing 360° by the number of sides of the relevant polygon. For example, for a pentagon, a 5-sided figure, dividing 5 into 360° gives an angle of 72°. This angle is the angle **subtended** at the centre by drawing lines from the side as in Fig. 16d. From this starting point we can determine all the other angles within the pentagon (Fig. 16e).

It can be seen that the external angles of the pentagon are the same as those subtended from the centre and that the angles on the base side are also equal.

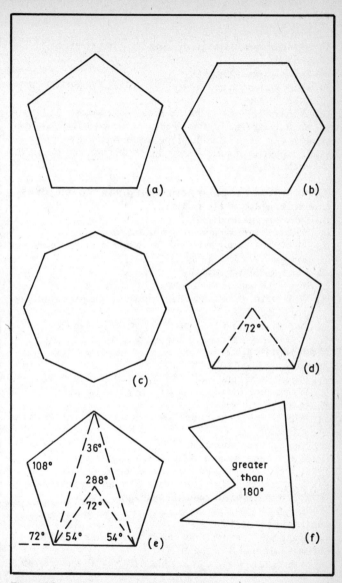

Figure 16

43

Construction of polygons

To inscribe a regular pentagon in a given circle (Fig. 17a)

(a) Draw the given circle O.
(b) Draw horizontal and vertical centre lines AB and CD.
(c) Bisect AO at E.
(d) With centre E and radius EC draw an arc to cut AB at F.
(e) With centre C and radius CF draw an arc to cut the circle at G.
(f) Join CG. CG is one side of the required pentagon.
(g) Complete the figure by stepping off this distance around the circle.

To construct a regular pentagon given the length of one side. Method I (Fig. 17b)

(a) Draw the given side AB.
(b) With centre B, radius AB, scribe a semi-circle.
(c) Divide the semi-circle into as many equal parts as the polygon has sides, in this case, 5.
(d) Join B to the **second** division from C.
(e) Bisect AB and $B2$ to meet at D.
(f) With centre D and radius DA draw a circle to pass through points B and 2.
(g) Step off AB around the circle to give the pentagon.

Method II (Fig. 17c)

(a) Draw the given side AB.
(b) With centre A and radius AB draw a circle.
(c) With centre B and radius BA draw a circle to cut the first circle at C and D.
(d) With centre D and radius AB draw an arc to cut the circles at E and F.
(e) Join CD to cut this arc at G.
(f) Join EG and produce to H on circle about centre B.
(g) Join FG and produce to J on circle about centre A.
(h) With centres J, H and radius AB draw arcs to intersect at K.
(i) Join $AJKHB$ to complete the pentagon.

Method III (Fig. 17d)

(a) Using a protractor set out angles of $108°$ from A and B.
(b) Make AE and BC equal to AB.
(c) With centres E and C and radius AB scribe arcs to intersect at D.
(d) $ABCDE$ is the required pentagon.

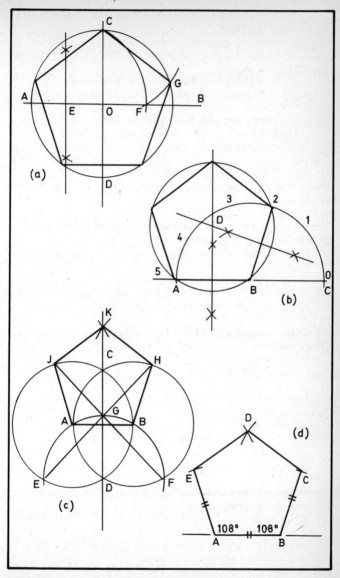

Figure 17

45

To construct a regular hexagon given the length of one side (Fig. 18a)

(a) Draw the given line AB.
(b) With centres A and B and radius AB scribe arcs intersecting at O.
(c) From O and with the same radius describe a circle.
(d) Set off AB around the circumference to complete the figure.

To construct a regular hexagon within a circle (Fig. 18b)

(a) Draw the given circle.
(b) The radius of the circle can be stepped off six times around the circumference.

Note This is a most useful fact to know when constructing hexagons.

To construct a regular hexagon given the distance across its flats (Fig. 18c)

(a) Draw a circle whose diameter equals the distance across the flats.
(b) Draw horizontal and vertical centre lines.
(c) Using a $30°$-$60°$ set-square draw lines tangential to the circle.

To draw a regular octagon on a given line (Fig. 18d)

(a) Draw the given line AB.
(b) Draw AH and BC with a $45°$ set-square, making them equal in length to AB.
(c) Erect perpendiculars AF and BE.
(d) Draw HG and CD parallel to them, making them equal in length to AB.
(e) With centres G and D and radius AB scribe arcs to cut the perpendiculars at E and F.
(f) Join F and E. $ABCDEFGH$ is the required figure.

To construct a regular octagon given the distance across the corners (Fig. 18e)

(a) Draw a circle whose diameter is equal to the distance across the corners.
(b) Draw horizontal and vertical centre lines AB and CD intersecting at O.
(c) Through O draw diagonals EF and GH at $45°$.
(d) Join points to give the octagon $ABCDEFGH$.

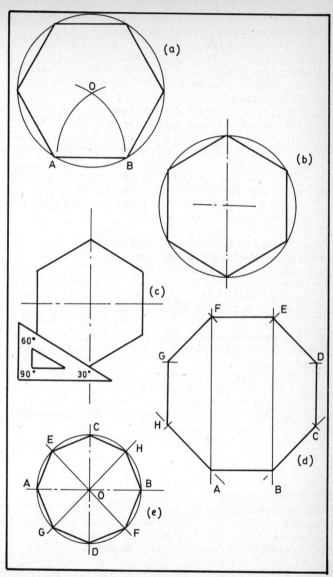

Figure 18

To construct a regular polygon of any number of sides within a given circle (Fig. 19a)

(a) Let the figure be a pentagon.
(b) Draw the given circle of diameter AB.
(c) Divide the diameter into the number of sides that the polygon has, in this case 5.

Note Use the method as in Fig. 6c.

(d) With centre A and radius AB draw an arc.
(e) With centre B and radius AB draw an arc to cut the previous one in E.
(f) From E draw a line through the **second** division on AB to cut the circle at F.

Note No matter how many divisions there are on AB it is always through the **second** one that the line from E is taken.

(g) AF is one side of the pentagon and this distance is stepped around the circle to produce the figure.

To construct a regular polygon of any number of sides given the length of one side (Fig. 19b)

(a) Let the figure be a pentagon.
(b) Draw the given side AB.
(c) Bisect AB at C.
(d) With centre C and radius CA draw an arc to cut the bisector DE at F.
(e) With centre A and radius AB draw an arc to cut DE at G.

Note Points F and G can be obtained by the use of 60° and 45° set-squares as shown in Fig. 19c.

(f) Bisect FG at H.
(g) Points F, H and G represent 4, 5 and 6 and are the centre points for whichever polygon is required.
(h) With centre 5 and radius $5A$ scribe a circle to pass through A and B.
(i) The length AB can be stepped off around the circle to give the required pentagon.

Key terms

Regular Polygon that has equal sides and equal angles.
Irregular Polygon whose angles and sides are unequal.
Diagonal A line from one corner to the opposite corner.
Subtended The angle at the centre, **opposite** to a side.

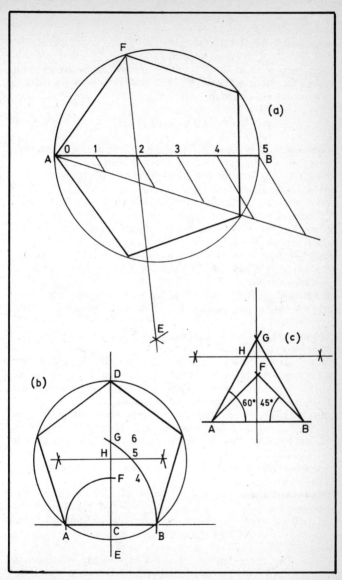

Figure 19

Chapter 7
Circles and tangents

A circle is a plane figure bounded or enclosed by a curved line called the **circumference.** The circumference is always equidistant from the **centre** of the circle.

Figure 20 shows the various parts of a circle.

Diameter Any straight line drawn through the centre of a circle and touching the circumference at both ends.

Radius Any straight line from the centre of the circle to any point on the circumference.

Arc Any part of the circumference of a circle.

Chord A straight line joining any two points on the circumference of the circle. The bisector of any chord passes through the centre of the circle.

Sector Part of a circle formed by drawing two radii and the arc which they cut off. This divides the circle into the major and minor sectors.

Segment Part of a circle bounded by a chord and an arc of the circle. The chord divides the circle into major and minor segments.

Quadrant An arc of a circle formed when two radii are drawn at 90° to one another.

Semi-circle Half a circle, formed either side of the diameter.

Tangent A straight line which touches, but does not cut, the circle. The exact point at which it touches the circle is known as the point of tangency or point of contact.

Normal The radius from the centre of the circle to the point of tangency. The tangent is always perpendicular to the normal.

Concentric circles Circles having the same centre but different radii, i.e., their circumferences are parallel.

Eccentric circles Circles of varying radii, each of which has a different centre.

Circumscribed circle (or circumcircle) A circle drawn round a figure so that it touches every point of that figure.

Inscribed circle A circle drawn inside a figure so that it touches the boundary surfaces of that figure.

Note The circumference of a circle is nearly $3\frac{1}{7}$ times its diameter or 3.1416 its diameter, usually shown by the Greek letter π (pi).

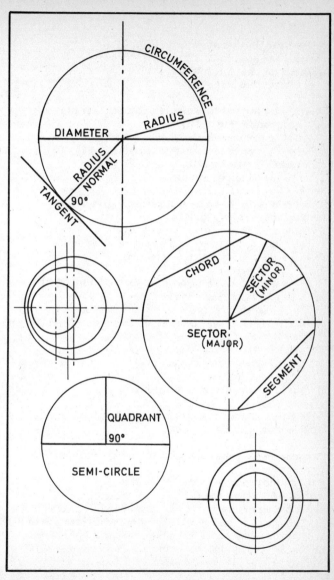

Figure 20

51

Constructions

To find the centre of a circle (Fig. 21a)
(a) Draw any two chords AB and CD.
(b) Bisect the chords to intersect at E.
(c) E is the centre of the circle.

To draw a tangent to a circle at a point on the circumference (Fig. 21b)
(a) Let A be the point on the circumference.
(b) Draw OA and produce so that $OA = AB$
(c) Bisect OB and draw CD.
(d) CD is the required tangent.

To draw a tangent to a circle from a given point P outside the circle (Fig. 21c)
(a) Draw a line from O to the given point P.
(b) Describe a semi-circle on OP to cut the circle in A.
(c) Join AP which is the required tangent.

To draw a tangent to two equal circles (Fig. 21d)
(a) Draw the two circles A and B.
(b) Join AB and bisect at C.
(c) Bisect AC at D and describe a semi-circle on AC to cut circle A at E.
(d) Join AE.
(e) From B draw a line parallel to AE to cut circle centre B at F.
(f) Join EF for the **internal tangent.**

Note If the tangent is **external,** the perpendiculars from A and B give the points of contact.

To draw an external tangent to two unequal circles (Fig. 21e)
(a) Draw the two unequal circles A and B.
(b) Join AB and bisect at C.
(c) With centre C and radius AC describe a semi-circle on AB.
(d) With centre B draw a circle equal to the **difference** of the two radii of the circles to cut the semi-circle at D.
(e) Join BD and produce to cut the circle with centre B at E.
(f) From A draw AF parallel to BE.
(g) Join EF.
(h) EF is the external tangent.

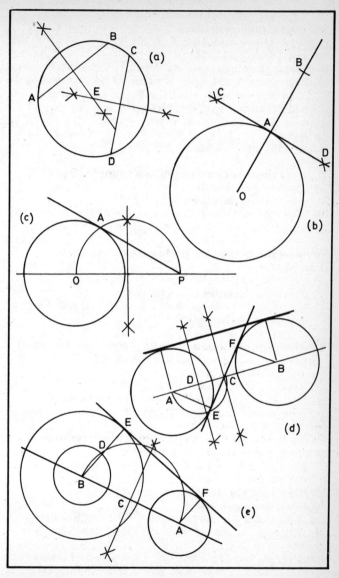

Figure 21

To draw the internal (or interior) tangent to two unequal circles (Fig. 22a)

(a) Draw the two unequal circles *A* and *B*.

(b) Join *AB* and bisect at *C*.

(c) With centre *C* and radius *AC* describe a semi-circle.

(d) With centre *B* and radius the **sum** of the two radii of the given circles, draw a circle to cut the semi-circle at *D*.

(e) Join *BD* to cut the circle with centre *B* at *E*.

(f) From *A* draw *AF* parallel to *BD*.

(g) Join *EF*.

(h) *EF* is the internal tangent.

To draw the inscribed circle to a triangle (Fig. 22b)

(a) Draw the triangle *BAC*.

(b) Bisect any two **angles** to meet at *O*.

(c) With centre *O* and radius *OD* (perpendicular to *AB*), describe the circle to touch all three sides.

To draw the circumscribed circle to a triangle (Fig. 22c)

(a) Draw the triangle *ABC*.

(b) Bisect any two **sides** to meet at *O*.

(c) With centre *O* and radius *OA* draw the circle to touch all three points *A*, *B* and *C*.

To draw a circle to touch three given lines (Fig. 22d)

(a) Draw the three given lines *AB*, *CD* and *EF*.

(b) Produce them until they meet.

(c) Bisect the angles formed to meet at *O*.

(d) From *O* drop a perpendicular to one of the lines at *G*.

(e) With centre *O* and radius *OG* describe the required circle.

To draw a circle to pass through a given point and to touch a line at a given point (Fig. 22e)

(a) Draw a line *AB* and let *C* be the point on that line.

(b) Position the given point.

(c) Draw a perpendicular *CD* to the line *AB*.

(d) Join *C* to the given point *P*.

(e) Make angle *CPE* equal to angle *DCP* so that *PE* cuts *DC* at *O*.

(f) With centre *O* and radius *OC* draw the required circle.

Note Having joined the line *CP*, this could now be a chord of the circle. Bisect *CP* to meet *CD* at *O* to find the centre of the required circle.

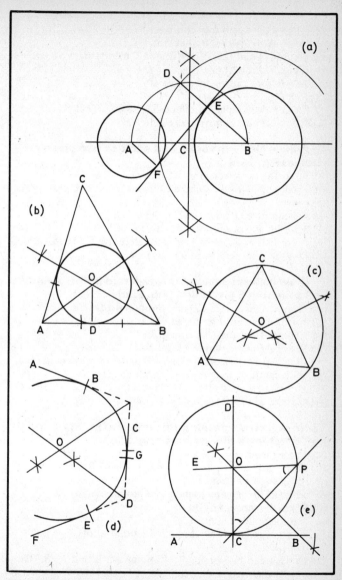

Figure 22

To inscribe a circle in a given angle which will also pass through a given point P (Fig. 23a)

(a) Draw angle *ABC* and bisect to *Q*.
(b) With any point *D* as centre draw a circle touching *AB* and *BC*. (From *D* drop a perpendicular to line *BC* to obtain radius).
(c) Join *P* to *B*, cutting this circle at *E*.
(d) Join *DE*.
(e) From *P* draw a line parallel to *DE* to cut *BQ* at *F*.
(f) *F* is the centre of the required circle.

To draw a circle to touch and enclose two given circles (Fig. 23b)

(a) Draw the two given circles *C* and *D*.
(b) From any point *A* on circle *C* draw a line *AB* to pass through centre *C*.
(c) From centre *D* draw *DE* parallel to *AB*.
(d) Join *AE* and produce to cut circle *D* at *F*.
(e) From *F* draw a line passing through centre *D* to cut *AB* at *O*.
(f) *O* is the centre of the required circle.

To draw a circle passing through two points A and B and touching a given line (Fig. 23c)

(a) Draw the given line *CD* and position the two points.
(b) Join *AB* and produce to cut *CD* at *E*.
(c) Extend *BE* so that *BE* equals *EF*.
(d) Bisect *AF* and describe a semi-circle.
(e) Drop a perpendicular from *E* to cut the semi-circle in *G*.
(f) With centre *E* and radius *EG* draw an arc to cut *CD* in *H*.
(g) Draw a perpendicular at *H* to meet the bisector of *AB* at *O*.
(h) *O* is the centre of the required circle.

To draw a circle passing through two points A and B and touching a given circle (Fig. 23d)

(a) Draw the given circle and the two points *A* and *B*.
(b) Draw any circle passing through *A* and *B* and cutting the given circle at *C* and *D*.
(c) Join *CD* and extend to meet *AB* produced at *E*.
(d) Draw the tangent *EF* to the given circle.
(e) *F* is the point of contact.
(f) Draw a circle passing through the three points *A*, *B* and *F*.

Note This can be obtained by joining *A*, *B* and *F*, *B*. These become two chords of a circle. Bisect *FB* and *AB* to meet at *O*. *O* is the centre of the required circle.

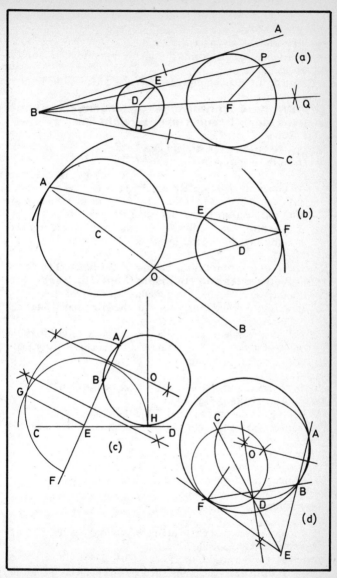

Figure 23

To draw an arc of given radius (R) to two straight lines (Fig. 24a)

(a) Draw the two given lines AB and CD.
(b) Draw lines parallel to and distance R away from AB and CD to meet at E.
(c) With centre E and radius R scribe an arc to meet the lines.

To draw an arc of given radius (R) tangential to a circle of given radius (r) and a given straight line (Fig. 24b)

(a) Let AB be the given straight line.
(b) Draw the given circle with centre C.
(c) Draw a line DE parallel to AB such that its distance from AB equals the radius of the required arc.
(d) With centre C and radius equal to that of the required arc **plus** the given arc ($r + R$) scribe an arc to cut DE at F.
(e) With centre F and radius R draw the required arc to touch both the line AB and the given arc.

To draw an arc of a given radius (r) tangential to two given circles and enclosing them (Fig. 24c)

(a) Let the two circles be A and B and their radii R and R_1.
(b) With centre A and radius equal to the given radius **less** the radius of A, i.e., ($r - R$), scribe an arc.
(c) With centre B and radius equal to the given radius **less** the radius of B, i.e., ($r - R_1$), scribe an arc to cut the first one in O.
(d) With centre O and radius r draw the required arc.

To draw an arc of a given radius (r) tangential to two given circles (Fig. 24d)

(a) Let the two circles be A and B and their radii R and R_1.
(b) With centre A and radius equal to r **plus** the radius of circle A i.e., ($r + R$), scribe an arc.
(c) With centre B and radius r **plus** the radius of circle B, i.e., ($r + R_1$), scribe an arc to cut the first one at O.
(d) With centre O and radius r draw the required arc.

Key terms

Pi   Circumference of a circle in relation to its diameter.
External   On the outside.
Internal   On the inside.
Point of contact   The point where a tangent meets the normal at the circumference.

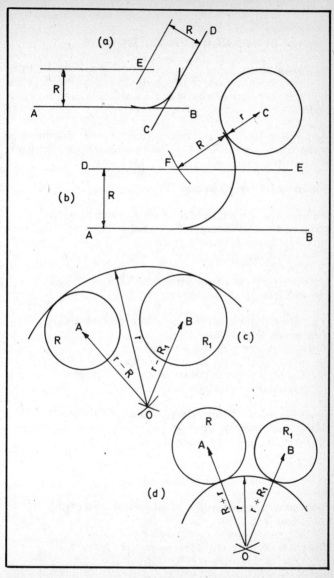

Figure 24

Chapter 8
Equal areas and similar figures

The **area** of any figure is the amount of space enclosed by or within its boundary. Area is measured in square centimetres, square inches, etc., according to the linear measurement of the figure.

A **similar** figure is one which has the same **shape** as a given figure but is not of the same size. The similar figure is enlarged or reduced in proportion to the original.

Figures of equal areas

To construct a triangle on a given base equal in area to a given triangle (Fig. 25a)
(a) Draw the given triangle *ABC*.
(b) Produce *AB* to *D* so that *AD* equals the given base. Join *CD*.
(c) Through *B* draw a line parallel to *CD* to cut *AC* in *E*.
(d) Join *DE*. *ADE* is the required triangle.

To construct a triangle equal in area to a given rectangle (Fig. 25b)
(a) Draw the given rectangle *ABCD*.
(b) Draw a line *EF* parallel to *AB* such that *AD* = *DE*.
(c) The point *G* can be positioned anywhere along *EF*.
(d) *AGB* is the required triangle.

To construct a triangle equal in area to a given quadrilateral (Fig. 25c)
(a) Draw the given quadrilateral *ABCD*. Join *BD*.
(b) Through *C* draw a line parallel to *BD* to cut *AB* produced in *E*.
(c) Join *DE*. *ADE* is the required triangle.

To construct a triangle equal in area to a regular polygon (Fig. 25d)
(a) Draw the given polygon *ABCDE*.
(b) Draw *FG* equal to the perimeter of the polygon.
(c) Join *F* and *G* to the centre of the polygon at *O*.
(d) *FOG* is the required triangle but can be modified in shape by doubling the height and halving the base.

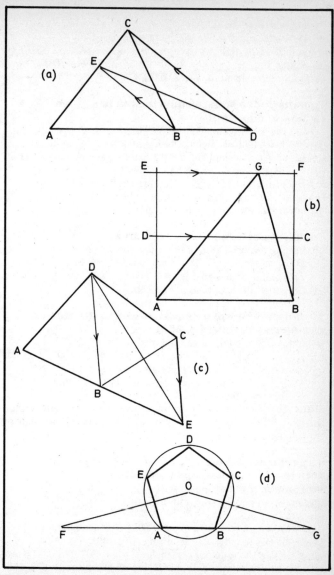

Figure 25

To construct a triangle equal in area to two given triangles (Fig. 26a)

(a) Let ABC and DEF be the given triangles.

(b) Join the two triangles to form the irregular polygon $ABEFD$.

(c) Using Fig. 25c as the basic proof, reduce $ABEFD$ to a quadrilateral and then to a triangle.

To construct a square equal in area to a given rectangle (Fig. 26b)

(a) Let the given rectangle be $ABCD$.

(b) Produce AB to E such that BE equals BC.

(c) Bisect AE in F and with centre F draw a semi-circle on AE.

(d) Produce BC to cut the semi-circle in G.

(e) BG is one side of the required square $BGHK$.

Note BG is the mean proportional between the sides of the rectangle AB and BE ($AB \times BE = BG^2$).

To construct a square of given area

(a) Let the required area of the square be 9.5 cm^2.

(b) Draw rectangle $ABCD$, 9.5 cm long by 1 cm broad.

(c) This rectangle has an area of 9.5 cm^2.

(d) Construct the square as in Fig. 26b.

To construct a square equal in area to the sum of two given squares (Fig. 26c)

(a) Let A and B be the given squares.

(b) Draw the right-angled triangle CDE such that CD equals the sides of square A and DE equals the sides of square B.

(c) The side CE will be one side of the required square $CEFG$ (Pythagoras' theorem).

Note The theorem of Pythagoras says that in a right-angled triangle the square on the hypotenuse is equal to the sum of the squares on the other two sides.

To construct a rectangle of unit breadth equal in area to a given rectangle (Fig. 26d)

(a) Draw the given rectangle $ABCD$.

(b) Draw AE equal to the unit breadth.

(c) Draw EF parallel to AB.

(d) Draw AF and produce to meet DC produced in G.

(e) Draw GK parallel to AD cutting EF produced in H.

(f) $EHKA$ is the required rectangle.

Note If the given rectangle $ABCD$ has less than the unit breadth extend AD to E and proceed as in Fig. 26e.

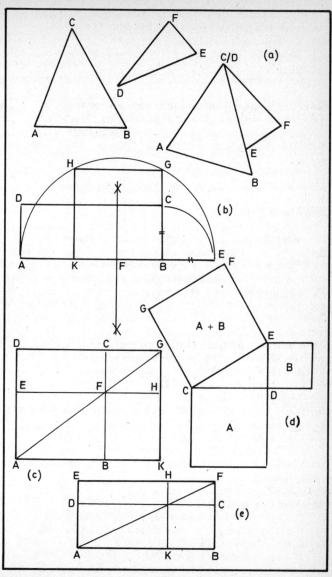

Figure 26

To divide a triangle into two equal areas by a line drawn from a given point on one side (Fig. 27a)
(a) Let the triangle be *ABC* and the point *D*.
(b) Bisect *AB* in *E* and join *CE*.
(c) Join *DE* and draw *CF* parallel to it.
(d) Join *DF* which divides the triangle into two equal areas.

To divide a quadrilateral into two equal areas by a line drawn through one of its angles (Fig. 27b)
(a) Let the quadrilateral be *ABCD* and the angle *D*.
(b) Draw the diagonals.
(c) Bisect *AC* in *E*.
(d) Draw *FG* parallel to *DB*.
(e) Join *DG* which divides *ABCD* into two equal areas.

Similar figures

A similar figure is one which has the same **shape** as a given figure but is not the same size or area. A similar figure can be drawn with either its **sides** or its **area** in a given ratio to the original. The constructions required to enlarge or reduce the length of sides in a given ratio are very different to those constructions required to enlarge or reduce the figure in ratio to area.

To construct a figure similar to a given figure but having sides 5:3 the length of the original
Method I (Fig. 27c)
(a) Draw the given figure *ABCDE*.
(b) From *A* draw *AC* and *AD*.
(c) Divide *AB* into 3 equal parts (by acute division line *AF*), (see Fig. 6c).
(d) Extend *AF* to *G* by two further units and draw *GH*.
(e) *AH* is in the ratio of 5:3 with *AB*.
(f) From *H* draw lines parallel to *BC*, *CD* and *DE* extended at *J*, *K* and *L*.
(g) *AHJKL* is the required figure.
Method II (Fig. 27d)
(a) Draw *ABCDE* and position point *P* inside the figure.
(b) Join *P* to each corner but divide *AP* into 3 equal parts.
(c) Extend *PA* by two further units to *PH*.
(d) *PH* is in the ratio of 5:3 with *PA*.
(e) From *H* draw parallel lines around *ABCDE* to meet the lines radiating from *P* in *HJKLM*.

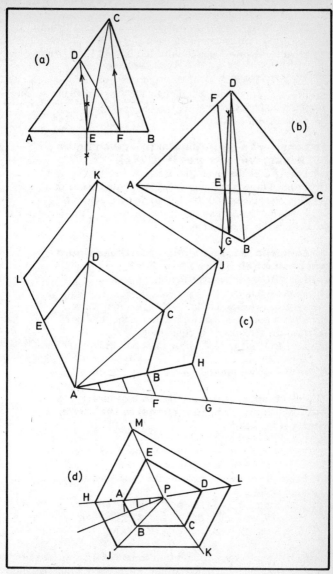

Figure 27

65

Method III (Fig. 28a)
(a) Draw *ABCDE* and position point *P* outside the figure.
(b) Join *P* to each corner of the figure.
(c) Divide *PA* into 3 equal units and extend by 2 further units to *PF*.
(d) *PA* to *PF* is 3:5.
(e) From *F* draw lines parallel to the original figure to meet the radial lines from *P* in *FGHJK*.
(f) *FGHJK* is the required figure.

To construct a figure similar to a given figure but having twice its area (Fig. 28b)
(a) Let *ABC* be the given triangle.
(b) From *A* draw a perpendicular, *AD*, equal in length to *AB*.
(c) Join *BD* and extend *BA* to *E* so that *BE* equals *BD*.
(d) From *E* draw *EF* parallel to *AC* meeting *BC* produced in *F*.
(e) *EBF* is the required figure.

To construct a figure similar to a given figure but having half its area (Fig. 28c)
(a) Let *ABCD* be the given figure.
(b) Bisect *AB* in *E*.
(c) With centre *E* and radius *AE* draw a semi-circle.
(d) Drop a perpendicular from *E* to cut the semi-circle in *F*.
(e) Join *BF* and make *BG* equal to it.
(f) Join *BD* and from *G* draw lines parallel to *AD* and *DC* at *H* and *J*.
(g) *BGHJ* is the required figure.

To construct a figure similar to a given figure but having an area proportional to that given figure (Fig. 28d)
(a) Let *ABC* be the given figure.
(b) Divide one of the sides, say *AB*, into 5 equal parts.
(c) Draw a semi-circle on *AB*.
(d) Erect a perpendicular at the first division to cut the semi-circle at *D*.
(e) With radius *AD* and centre *A* scribe an arc to cut *AB* at *E*.
(f) Draw *EF* parallel to *BC*.
(g) *AEF* is one-fifth the area of *ABC*.

Note If a figure of say three-fifths the area of *ABC* was required, then the perpendicular (*d*) would have been from the third division to the semi-circle.

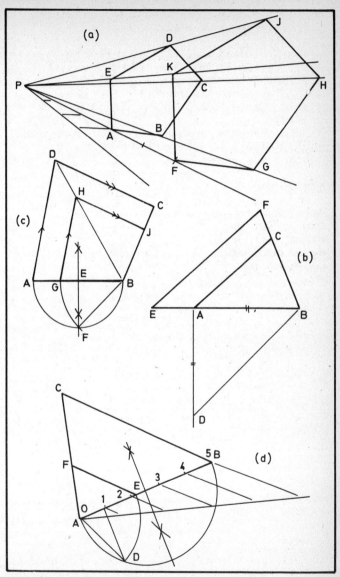

Figure 28

To construct a triangle similar to a given triangle but with its area increased in a given ratio (Fig. 29)

(a) Let ABC be the triangle.

(b) Let the increase be in the ratio of $7:5$.

(c) Mark off BD and BE in the ratio of $7:5$.

(d) Draw semi-circles on AD and AE.

(e) Drop a perpendicular from B to cut the semi-circles at F and G.

(f) Join AG and draw FH parallel to it to cut BA produced at H.

(g) Draw HJ parallel to AC to cut BC produced in J.

(h) HBJ is the required triangle.

Key terms

Area   Amount of space enclosed by a boundary.
Similar   Same shape.
Proportional   In ratio.
Radial or radiating   Straight lines from the same centre extending outwards.

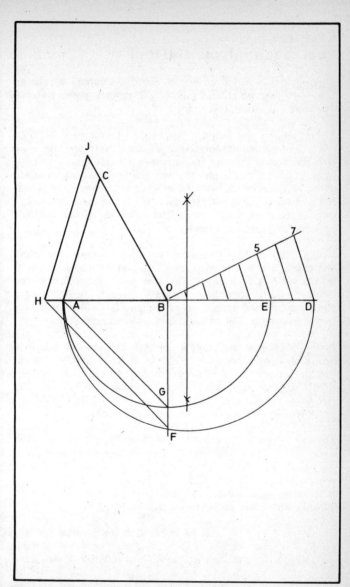

Figure 29

Chapter 9
Loci mechanisms and loci

A point that moves from one position to another, in relation to some other point and following a definite path, traces a line known as a locus (plural loci).

In engineering and industry the need to know these paths or traces is of paramount importance because every machine must have freedom of movement of a part in relation to another part. In an engine, for example, the four main mechanisms involved would be the relationship between cylinder, piston, connecting-rod and crank. It is essential that these four mechanisms can work together without becoming entangled when following their very own different movements.

In Fig. 30a, as the piston A moves up and down, the crank will rotate about a fixed point C. Therefore, the locus of B in relation to C is a circle. The locus of A in relation to the cylinder is a straight line. However, to plot the locus of a point P positioned upon the connecting-rod, it will be necessary to plot its path in relation to the facts or loci already known.

In Fig. 30b, draw the straight line AC and position the circle centre C with radius BC. Divide the circle into at least eight regular distances along its circumference. As the point B moves to B_1 the position of A will alter. Upon each line representing AB, A_1B_1, A_2B_2, etc., plot the point P and join P_1, P_2, P_3, etc., together. We now have the locus of point P.

The moving parts of a machine are generally held or pivoted in some way to one another. In tracing a path or locus it is essential to know the exact nature of this connection or pivoting otherwise loci cannot be determined accurately. Some connections or pivots can slide, oscillate, rotate or may only pivot on a fixed point. Some examples are given in Fig. 30c.

There are very few rules to learn about loci, rather, it is a question of common sense. Make sure you plot the movement carefully and number each of the points as you mark them out.

The path or trace of the locus may be a straight line, a curve or a combination of both.

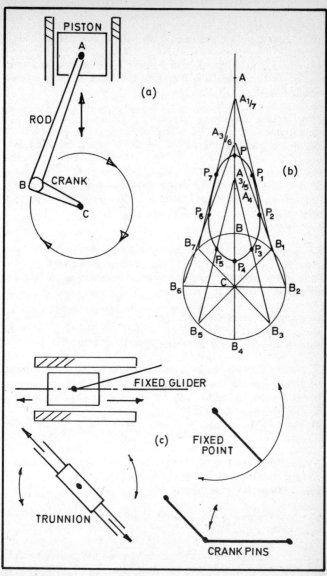

Figure 30

For example:

(a) A ball thrown in the air traces an arc in relation to the ground and therefore the locus of the ball is a curve (Fig. 31a).

(b) A lead shot dropped from a tower traces a straight line in relation to the tower and therefore the locus of the shot is a straight line (Fig. 31b).

(c) A model car racing around a 'chain-link' track traces straight lines as well as semi-circles in relation to the centre line of the track. The locus of the car is a parallel-sided oval (Fig. 31c).

(d) A cyclist's foot on a moving pedal traces a series of circles which have a relation to the centre of the crank of the moving pedal and to the ground. The locus of the foot is a series of loops (Fig. 31d).

These are very simple loci, but in order to be able to plot any locus, it is essential to know the exact position of the given point and to know the conditions and limitations governing the movement of that point.

As a further example, let us look at Fig. 31e. The pole XY moves such that X slides down to A whilst Y slides out to B. We are required to plot the locus of the point P on XY.

(a) Divide XA into a convenient number, say 8 (the more divisions made, the greater the accuracy).
(b) As X moves down to X_1 so XY, which is a fixed distance, will move along towards B at Y_1.
(c) Move X_1 to X_2 and so on, each time taking the fixed distance XY and stepping off this distance along the ground line.
(d) Each time the line XY, X_1Y_1, X_2Y_2, etc., has been recorded so P can be positioned at P_1, P_2, P_3, etc.
(e) The locus of P is seen to be a curve.

A locus is defined as the path traced out by a point which moves under definite conditions.

There are several loci which are given special names because the conditions which govern their movement give rise to predictable curves.

72

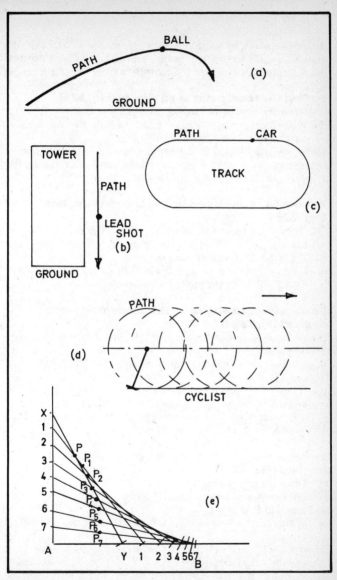

Figure 31

73

Ellipse

An ellipse is the locus of a point which moves so that the sum of its distance from two fixed points, known as the **focal points,** is a constant. The constant is the **major** axis of the ellipse.

To find the focal point of an ellipse (Fig. 32a)
(a) Draw the **major** and **minor** axes AB and CD.
(b) With centre C and radius equal to half the major axis, scribe arcs to cut AB at F_1 and F_2.

Note $F_1C + F_2C = AB$ and therefore satisfies the definition of an ellipse. Any point P on the ellipse must also satisfy this definition in that $F_1P + F_2P$ equals AB.

To construct an ellipse by the Trammel method (Fig. 32b)
(a) Draw the major and minor axes AB and CD.
(b) Mark off, on a piece of card or paper, half the major axis PR and half the minor axis QR.
(c) If P is always kept upon CD and Q is always kept upon AB, then R will trace the path of the ellipse.

To construct an ellipse by the concentric circle method (Fig. 32c)
(a) Draw the major and minor axes AB and CD and draw a circle on each.
(b) Divide the circles into equal parts by lines radiating from O.
(c) Where these lines cut the minor circle, draw horizontals and where they cut the major circle, draw perpendiculars.
(d) The intersections of the horizontal and perpendicular lines will be the points upon the ellipse.

To construct an ellipse by the approximate arc method (Fig. 32d)
(a) Draw major and minor axes AB and CD.
(b) With centre O and radius AO scribe an arc to cut OC produced in P. Join AC.
(c) With centre C and radius CP scribe an arc to cut AC in Q.
(d) Bisect AQ and this bisector will cut the major axis in R and the minor axis in S.
(e) R and S are the centres for circles which will give the ellipse.

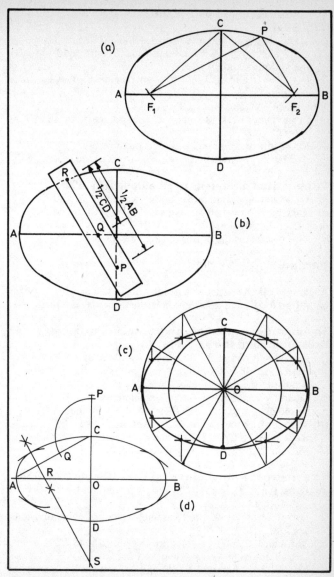

Figure 32

To construct an ellipse by the rectangle method (Fig. 33a)
(a) Draw the major and minor axes AB and CD.
(b) Draw a rectangle, $EFGH$, length and breadth equal to that of the major and minor axes.
(c) Divide AH and AO into the same number of equal parts, say four.
(d) Draw C_1, C_2 and C_3.
(e) From D, draw D_1 to meet C_1, D_2 to meet C_2 and D_3 to meet C_3.
(f) These intersections will be points on the ellipse.
(g) Repeat this process in the other quarters of the rectangle.

To construct a tangent to an ellipse (Fig. 33b)
(a) Draw an ellipse and position the focal points F_1 and F_2.
(b) Take any point P on the ellipse and join P to F_1 and F_2.
(c) Bisect the angle F_1PF_2.
(d) This bisector is the normal to the tangent at P.

Parabola

A parabola is the locus of a point whose distance from a fixed point (the focus) and a straight line (the directrix) is equal.

To construct a parabola given the directrix, the focal point and the axis (Fig. 33c)
(a) Draw the directrix XY, the focus F and the axis AB.
(b) Bisect AF at V (vertex). V is a point on the parabola as it satisfies the definition, $AV = VF$.
(c) Divide VB, as shown, into an equal number of divisions, say 5, and draw lines through these divisions parallel to XY.
(d) With centre F and radius $A-1$, scribe an arc to cut line 1 in a/a.
(e) Repeat for $A-2$, $A-3$, $A-4$ and $A-5$.
(f) The curve formed is a parabolic curve.

To construct a parabola within a rectangle (Fig. 33d)
(a) Draw the rectangle $ABCD$ and divide in half by XY (axis of symmetry).
(b) Divide DA and AY into the same number of equal divisions, say four.
(c) Through 1, 2 and 3 on AY draw lines parallel to XY.
(d) Draw lines from X to 1, 2 and 3 on DA.
(e) The intersections of 1/1, 2/2 and 3/3 are the points on the parabola.

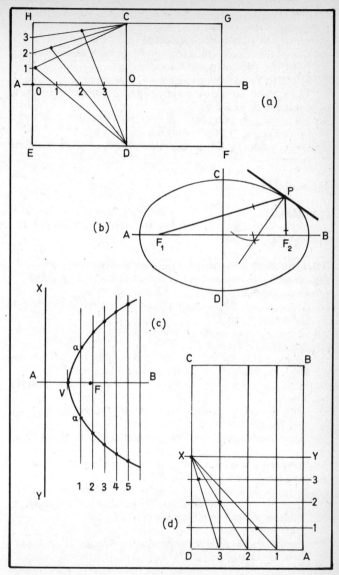

Figure 33

To construct a tangent from a point P outside the parabola and a tangent to a given point Q on the curve of the parabola (Fig. 34a)

(a) Draw the focus, directrix and vertex and construct a parabola. Position point P and Q.
(b) Join P to F and draw a circle with PF as diameter.
(c) Draw a line through the vertex, parallel to the directrix, to cut the circle at R and S.
(d) PR and RS are tangents to the parabola from P.
(e) Draw FQ and QT (QT being parallel to AB).
(f) Bisect angle TQF to obtain the tangent to Q on the curve of the parabola.

Hyperbola

A hyperbola is the locus of a point whose distance from a fixed point (the focus) to a straight line (the directrix) has a constant ratio greater than one.

To construct a hyperbola given the directrix, the focus and the ratio (unit of eccentricity) (Fig. 34b)

(a) Draw the directrix XY, focus F and axis AB.
(b) The vertex V will be positioned between AF in the ratio of the problem, say 3:1.
(c) Divide AF into 4 equal divisions and place V on the division nearest the directrix.
(d) Divide VB as shown into an equal number of divisions, say five, and through these divisions draw lines parallel to XY.
(e) With centre F and radius 3 times A–1 scribe an arc to cut line 1 in a/a.
(f) With centre F and radius 3 times A–2 scribe an arc to cut line 2 in b/b.
(g) Repeat for lines 3, 4 and 5 to obtain the hyperbolic curve.

To construct a hyperbola given the asymptotes and a point P on the curve (Fig. 34c)

(a) Draw the asymptotes AB and BC and position the given point P.
(b) Through P draw lines DE and FG parallel to BC and AB.
(c) Position points 1 and 2 anywhere on FG.
(d) From B draw lines through 1 and 2 to cut DE at 3 and 4.
(e) From 3 and 4 draw lines parallel to AB and from 1 and 2 draw lines parallel to BC.
(f) The intersections of lines 3 and 1 and 4 and 2 are points on the hyperbola.

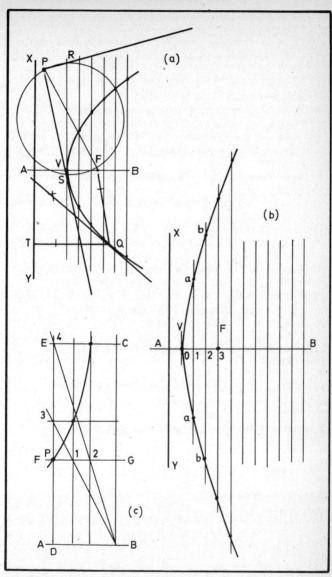

Figure 34

79

Cycloid

A cycloid is the locus of a point on the circumference of a circle which rolls, without slipping, along a fixed straight line.

To construct a cycloid (Fig. 35a)
(a) Draw the circle centre C and the fixed straight line AB.
(b) Position point P on the circumference of the circle.
(c) Divide the circumference of the circle into an equal number of divisions, say 8 and divide AB into this number of equal divisions.
(d) Draw lines through the divisions on the circumference parallel to AB.
(e) Erect perpendiculars from the divisions on AB to intersect these parallel lines.
(f) The circle moves along the line AB, revolving clockwise.
(g) The centre C will now be at C_1 and P will have moved from its original position.
(h) With centre C_1, radius CP, scribe an arc to cut the parallel line 7/1 of the circle. This is the new position of P_1.
(i) With centre C_2, radius CP, scribe an arc to cut the parallel line 6/2 of the circle. This is the next position of P_2.
(j) Repeat the process for further points.

Inferior trochoid (or curtate trochoid) (Fig. 35b)

The inferior trochoid is the locus of a point inside a circle which rolls, without slipping, along a fixed straight line.

Superior trochoid (or prolate trochoid) (Fig. 35c)

The superior trochoid is the locus of a point outside a circle.

Note In both cases, the trochoid is attached to the circle in a rigid fashion. Care must be taken when plotting both trochoids that the distance stepped off along the ground line is relevant to the circumference of the **motivating** circle and not the circle that contains point P.

Note The profile of rack-teeth on cast gears is based on the cycloid.

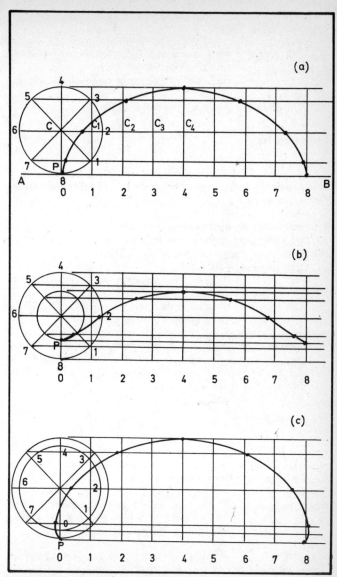

Figure 35

To construct a tangent and normal to a point P on a cycloid (Fig. 36a)

(a) Draw the cycloid and position point P.
(b) With centre P and radius the same as the rolling circle scribe an arc to cut the centre line in O.
(c) With centre O draw the rolling circle to touch the ground line in Q.
(d) PQ is the normal and XY the tangent (see Fig. 21b).

Epicycloid

An epicycloid is the locus of a point on the circumference of a circle which rolls around the **outside** of another **fixed circle,** without slipping.

To construct an epicycloid (Fig. 36b)

(a) Draw the circle centre D and the base circle centre C.
(b) Divide the circumference of the circle centre D into an equal number of divisions, say 8.
(c) Mark off from P these divisions upon the circumference of the base circle, in this case from A to B.
(d) With centre C and radius the points 7/1, 6/2, 5/3 and 4 on the small circle, draw parallel lines to AB.
(e) From C draw radiating lines through the divisions on AB to intersect the previously drawn parallel lines.
(f) These intersections will give all the necessary points to plot the curve, in a similar fashion to the drawing of the cycloid in Fig. 35a.

Hypocycloid

A hypocycloid is the locus of a point on the circumference of a circle when the circle rolls, without slipping, along the **inside** of another **fixed circle** (Fig. 36c).

The construction of the hypocycloid is very similar to that of the epicycloid, the difference being that the motivating circle is plotted on the inside of the fixed circle.

Note The circumference of any circle can be calculated **mathematically** but it is deemed sufficiently accurate to step off the distances with dividers (Fig. 36d).

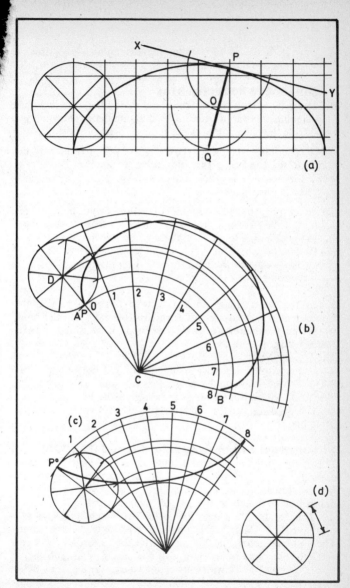

Figure 36

Helix

A helix is the locus of a point moving along and around a cylinder, the two movements being in a constant ratio.

To construct a helix (Fig. 37a)
(a) Draw two views of a cylinder and divide the end view into an equal number of parts, say 8, and number as shown.
(b) Divide the elevation of the cylinder into equal divisions.

Note The length taken by these divisions is governed by the length of the **lead** or **pitch,** this being the amount moved forward for 360° of angular movement (or the axial distance travelled in one revolution).

(c) Erect perpendiculars in the elevation from the numbers 0, 1, 2, 3, etc., and project parallel lines from the numbers in the end view to intersect these perpendicular lines.
(d) Plot points where 0/0, 1/1, 2/2, 3/3, etc., intersect.
(e) Each division of the lead (or pitch) represents a movement forward of $1/8$ of a revolution.

When the point travels in a clockwise direction around the cylinder, it is termed a **right-hand helix** and when the point travels in a counter-clockwise direction, it is called a **left-hand helix.**

The helix is of importance to engineers because of its use in the design of screws and springs. It is also the curve generated when turning between centres on a lathe. The lead screw on a lathe is an example of a square screw thread using the helical principle.

To construct a right-hand screw thread (Fig. 37b)
This is the formation of two cylinders, one of smaller diameter than the other. The diameter of the cylinders will depend on the diameter of the thread of the larger cylinder and the depth of the thread of the smaller cylinder. The procedure is the same as for the single line helix. Although the diameters of the helices differ, their pitch or lead must be the same. The distance across the thread will be the difference between the two diameters in order to give a square thread, and therefore a parallel helix will start that distance away from 0. In order to draw a single-start square thread it is simply a question of 'adding' the **core.**

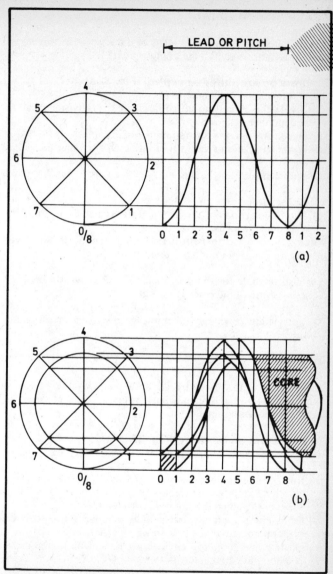

Figure 37

Archimedean spiral

An archimedean spiral is the locus of a point whose movement radially is uniform to its angular movement.

To draw an archimedean spiral (Fig. 38a)
(a) Draw a circle of diameter AB.
(b) Divide the circle into an equal number of divisions, say 8, and number as shown.
(c) Divide AB into the **same** number of divisions.
(d) With centre A and radius $A-1$ scribe an arc to cut the radial line 1.
(e) With centre A and radius $A-2$ scribe an arc to cut the radial line 2.
(f) Repeat around the circle.
(g) The intersections of the arcs and the radials gives the path traced by the locus.
Note This is for **one revolution** of the spiral; if two revolutions are required then AB is divided into 16.

It is also possible for the start of the spiral to be at a distance from the centre of the circle (Fig. 38b).

An application of this spiral is the groove on a gramophone record.

Involute

An involute is the locus traced by a point on the end of a straight line as that line unwinds from the circumference of a circle, without slipping.

To construct an involute (Fig. 38c)
(a) Draw the circle and divide it into a number of equal parts, say 8.
(b) Number the circle as shown and from 0/8 draw a tangent OC equal to the circumference of the circle (see Fig. 36d).
(c) Number the equal divisions as shown on OC.
(d) From point 1 on the circle draw a tangent to the circle at that point equal in length to 1-8 on OC.
(e) From point 2 on the circle draw a tangent to the circle at that point equal in length to 2-8 on OC.
(f) Repeat around the circle until the locus is plotted.
Note This spiral curve is used in the design of gear teeth.

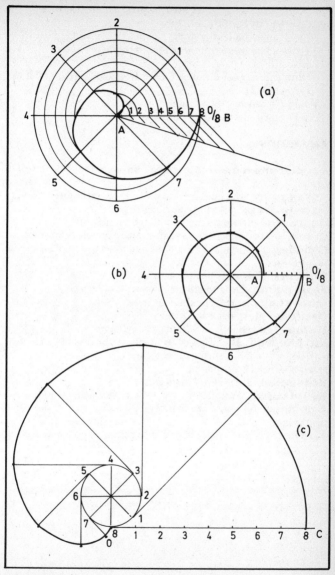

Figure 38

To construct a tangent and normal to an involute at a point P (Fig. 39)

(a) Draw an involute to a circle.
(b) Draw a line from P to the centre of the base circle.
(c) Bisect PO at Q.
(d) With centre Q and radius QO draw a semi-circle to cut the base circle at T.
(e) Join PT which is the normal.
(f) XY is the tangent to this normal.

Key terms

Angular movement Movement through the degrees of a circle.

Asymptotes The lines used to plot a given hyperbolic curve.

Axis (plural axes) Centre line of a figure.

Concentric circles Circles with the same centre.

Crank An arm attached to a shaft to give a reciprocating motion.

Cylinder The tubular chamber in which the piston of an engine reciprocates.

Directrix The polar line or plane of a locus.

Focal points Used to plot an ellipse.

Motivating circle The driving circle.

Oscillate Move back and forth.

Piston The metal piece within a car cylinder.

Pitch or lead The distance from one screw thread to the next or from one coil in a spring to the next.

Pivot A rotary movement.

Revolution Turning about an axis.

Spiral curve Winds about and away from a central point.

Symmetry (opposite asymmetry) Even on either side of a centre line.

Trammel Used to plot ellipses; also refers to a beam compass.

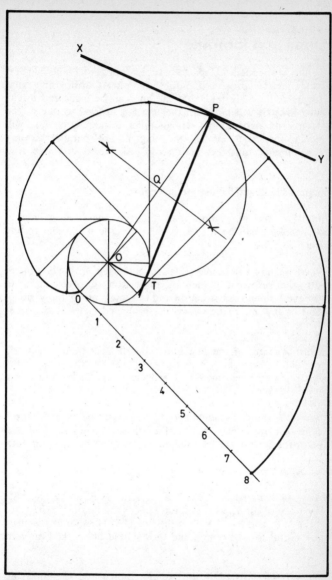

Figure 39

Chapter 10
Lines and laminae

A line suspended in space between horizontal and vertical planes can be projected onto those planes orthographically. However, the only time that the line can be measured for its **true length** will be when the line is **parallel** to one of the **planes of projection.** In all other instances the line will appear foreshortened. If the line is not parallel to any plane, then it must be made so in order to ascertain its true length.

Figures 40a, b and c illustrate this point.

Similarly, the only time that the true angle of inclination to any plane can be found is when the line is parallel to any plane (Fig. 40d).

When dealing with lines in space that have an inclination to both the principal planes of projection, it is essential to plot every line of construction and to remember that any movement in any one plane affects the projected views in the other planes.

The movement of the line into a parallel position, to say the horizontal plane (known as the H.P.), affects the view in the vertical (known as the V.P.) and end vertical (known as the E.V.P.) planes.

Figure 40e shows a straight line AB suspended between the three planes of reference. When the pictorial view is laid flat (known as rabatment) the orthographic views can be seen (Fig. 40f).

A trace is the line resulting from the intersection of two planes.

In Fig. 40f the trace of the V.P. and the H.P. is the line OX. The trace of the E.V.P. and the H.P. is the line OY. The trace of the V.P. and the E.V.P. is the line OZ. These lines are often very useful for references and they should be marked on your drawings.

The reference to O is not usually shown and the lines are simply referred to as XY and YZ.

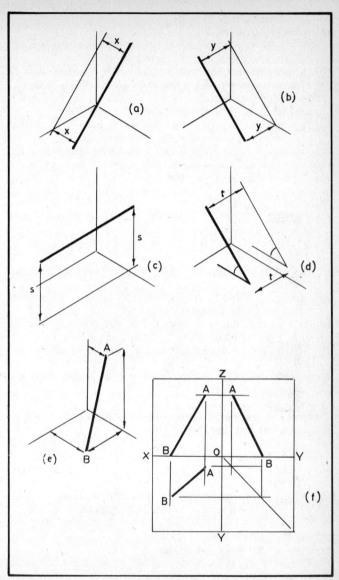

Figure 40

To construct a true length
Method I (Fig. 41a)
(a) *AB* is inclined to the three planes of reference and the figure shows the three orthographic views.
(b) In order to find the true length of *AB* it is necessary to make one view parallel to one of the planes of reference.
(c) In the plan, project the point *A* down to A_1 so that A_1B is parallel to the vertical plane (V.P.).
(d) Having done this the other two views have been altered and the new positions of A_1 have been projected.
(e) The true length of A_1B is seen in the front elevation view.
Note Although *A* was swung down to A_1 (in the plan view) it did not move off the horizontal plane.

Method II (Fig. 41b)
(a) The true length of *AB* can be determined by moving *B* instead of *A* as in Method I.
(b) In the plan, move *B* to B_1 so that AB_1 is parallel to the vertical plane (V.P.).
(c) Project the new position of B_1 from the plan into the other two views.
(d) Through *B* in the front elevation (F.E.) draw a line parallel to the horizontal plane (H.P.).
(e) This parallel line will meet the previous view projection of B_1 from the plan.
(f) AB_1 in the front elevation is the true length of the line *AB*.
Note Although *B* was moved in the plan, its height above the horizontal did not alter.

To find the traces of a line given the plan and elevation of the line (Fig. 41c)

To find the Horizontal Trace (h.t.)
(a) Produce the line *BA* in the front elevation to meet the line *XY* in *P*.
(b) Project *P* down to meet the line *BA* in the plan extended at *Q*.
(c) The point of intersection at *Q* is the horizontal trace.

To find the Vertical Trace (v.t.)
(a) Produce *AB* in the plan to meet *XY* in *R*.
(b) Project *R* up to meet the line *AB* in the front elevation, extended at *S*.
(c) The point of intersection at *S* is the vertical trace.

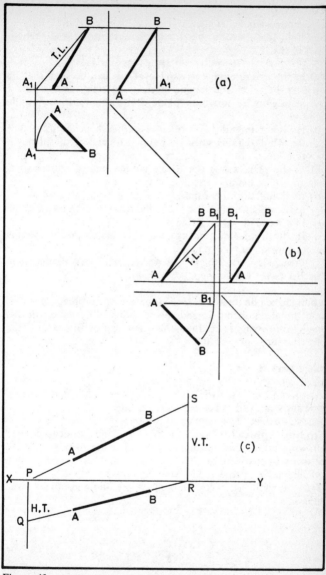

Figure 41

Laminae

It is also possible to project views of laminae (these have no apparent thickness) in space and to ascertain the true shape of the lamina.

(a) In the orthographic views (Fig. 42) it can be seen that the line BC is a true length in the plan only, as this line is resting on the horizontal plane. It must therefore be parallel to it.

(b) However in order to obtain the true shape of the figure, the whole lamina must be parallel to one of the planes of reference.

(c) In the plan, swing the whole lamina until C moves to C_1 and BC_1 is parallel to the E.V.P.

(d) In doing this the other views have been altered so that in the plan we have BA_1C_1, in the front elevation C_1BA_1 and in the end elevation BC_1A_1.

(e) In the front elevation project A_1 to A_2 so that the lamina is now upright and parallel to the E.V.P.

(f) Project A_2 across the E.V.P. and A_1 in the E.V.P. to meet it.

(g) BA_2C_1 is the true shape of the lamina.

Laminae can be treated as three separate line problems and each line treated individually and solved individually. One will then have three separate true lengths which can be drawn to obtain the true shape of the lamina.

Key terms

Angle of inclination The angle between a line and its base.
Foreshortened Less than the real length.
Intersection The meeting of two lines.
Orthographically Relative to two planes, concerned with drawing a three-dimensional object in two dimensions.
Planes of projection The horizontal and vertical planes onto which lines are projected for reference.
True length The actual length of any line and not its visual length.

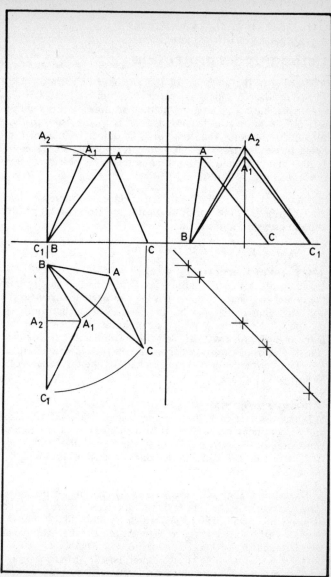

Figure 42

95

Section III Solid Geometry
Chapter 11
Orthographic projection

A drawing is the language of the engineer or architect who wishes to place his ideas on paper. He conveys the 3-D solid onto a flat surface. The usual method of drawing this solid or 3-D object into a two-dimensional one is by the use of orthographic projection. The solid or 3-D object is imagined as being suspended in space but with a relationship to planes or 'walls' that surround it on three sides. The object is then projected onto the walls.

A plane may be described as a flat surface and these surfaces are referred to as the **vertical plane,** the **horizontal plane** and the **end vertical plane.**

The means of projection has **two** forms:

1st-angle projection (Fig. 43a)
1st-angle projection is traditionally British and in this system the object suspended in space has lines projected **'through it'** onto the relative planes. What the eyes see from the front, top or side of the object is projected or drawn through onto the plane or wall **behind** it. The side view can be placed on either side of the front elevation depending on the view required. If the planes are now opened out and laid flat the three views can be seen as in Fig. 43b.

3rd-angle projection (Fig. 43c)
3rd-angle projection is used in the United States of America and in continental countries. British industry is now virtually committed to this system and eventually all countries will adopt it as the national and international means of orthographic projection.

In this system, the object suspended in space is not projected through, but is 'peered at', and the impression recorded on the 'transparent' plane. The result, which is rather like a 'mirror' image, is that the views have changed places when compared with 1st-angle projection (Fig. 43d). See also Figs. 44-47.

Note It is still possible to use either 1st- or 3rd-angle orthographic projection in examinations, although eventually, 3rd-angle will be the only projection used.

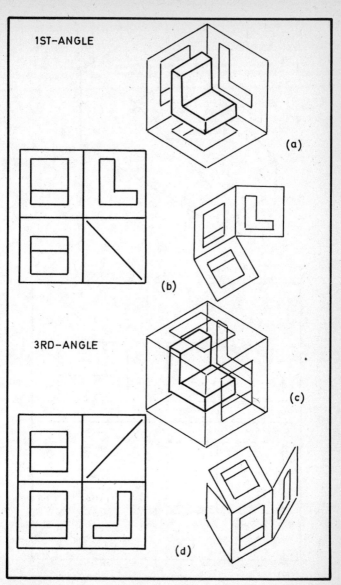

1ST-ANGLE

(a)

(b)

3RD-ANGLE

(c)

(d)

Figure 43

97

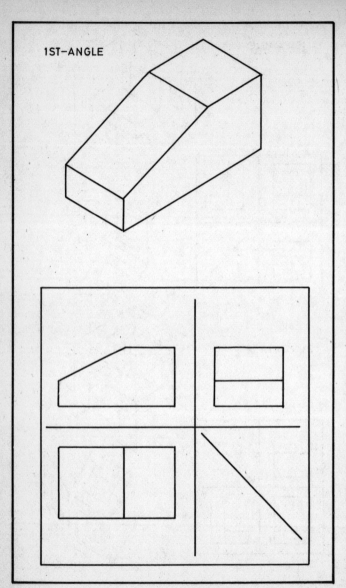

1ST-ANGLE

Figure 44

98

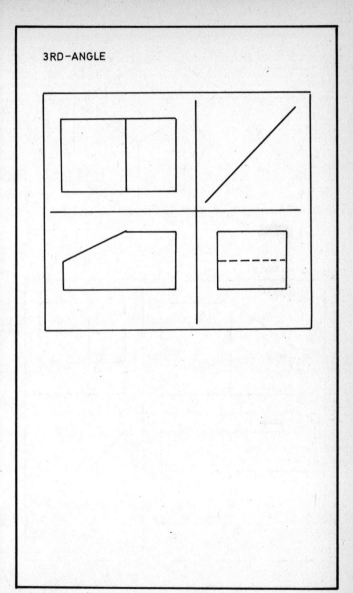

Figure 45

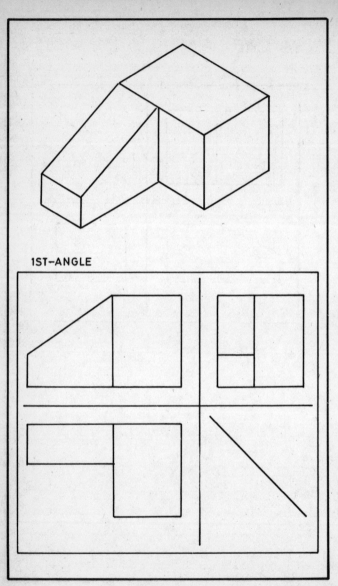

1ST–ANGLE

Figure 46

100

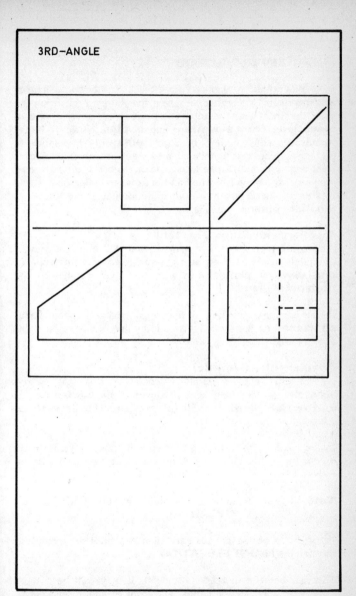

Figure 47

101

Chapter 12
Auxiliary projection

In orthographic projection the object is viewed at **right-angles** from a number of given positions, i.e., from the side, the front and the top. These views are known as **end elevations, front elevations** and the **plan.** However, it may be advantageous to view the object **obliquely** in relation to one of the planes. It may be advantageous to view the object at right-angles to an **oblique** surface on the object. In either case an auxiliary projection is needed and in order to make the drawing clearer it is necessary to introduce additional planes known as **auxiliary planes** (Fig. 48a).

Auxiliary elevations (Fig. 48b)
An auxiliary elevation is obtained when the object is viewed obliquely or other than at right-angles to the **vertical** or **end vertical planes,** but with the 'eye' parallel to the **horizontal plane.**

In the auxiliary elevation all lines projected will appear **foreshortened** except the heights and any line or surface at right-angles to the viewer.

Auxiliary plan (Fig. 48c)
An auxiliary plan is obtained when the object is viewed obliquely or other than at right-angles to the **horizontal** or **end vertical plane,** but with the 'eye' parallel to the **vertical plane.**

In the auxiliary plan, lines projected will appear foreshortened except the widths and any line or surface at right-angles to the viewer.

Note In order to obtain an auxiliary elevation the lines are projected through the **PLAN** view.

In order to obtain an auxiliary plan the lines are projected through the **FRONT ELEVATION** view.

This can be seen in Figs. 49 and 50. It may well be that an orthographic projection could have front elevation, end elevation, plan **plus** one or two auxiliary views.

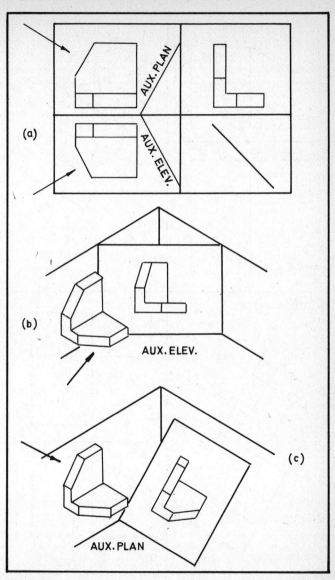

(a)

AUX. PLAN

AUX. ELEV.

(b)

AUX. ELEV.

(c)

AUX. PLAN

Figure 48

103

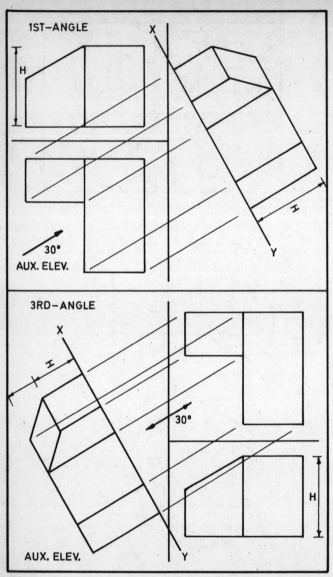

Figure 49

104

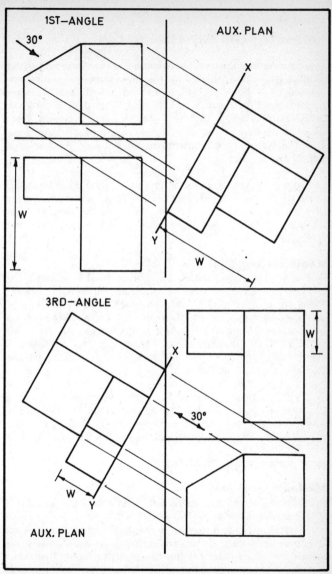

1ST—ANGLE

AUX. PLAN

30°

X

Y

W

W

3RD—ANGLE

X

30°

W

Y

W

W

AUX. PLAN

Figure 50

105

Chapter 13
Isometric/oblique projection

Engineering and technical drawing are always drawn in ortho-graphic projection, this being the most superior method yet devised. It is however difficult to understand these drawings if one is not fully conversant with them. The whole point about technical drawing is that it is the ability to convey one's ideas to somebody else who is perhaps a long distance away. It is the system of **communication** between one technical person and another.

In order to communicate at all levels it is sometimes necessary to draw a pictorial view of an object. There are many systems of pictorial presentation but the main two are isometric and oblique. In these views, three faces or surfaces are presented on the one 'picture' or view.

Isometric (Fig. 51a)
Isometric projection presents the more natural looking view of an object. In isometric drawing, there are three main axes and these are inclined at 120° to each other. One axis is vertical and the other two are at 30° to the horizontal. **All** isometric lines are at 30° to the horizontal or vertical and it is upon these lines only that distances or lengths can be measured. It can be seen therefore that all lines in isometric are parallel to one of the three main axes.

When attempting to draw an isometric it is often best to draw the 'overall' box into which the object would fit. This means taking the maximum height, width and length and drawing that pictorial view first. The details can then be fitted in (Fig. 51b).

Isometric circles (Fig. 51c)

Method I (ordinate)
(a) Draw the circle O in orthographic and encase it in a square.
(b) Draw the centre lines AB and CD.
(c) Divide the figure into equal divisions and number as shown.
(d) Draw the same size square as in (c) but draw in isometric.
(e) Divide in a similar fashion to the orthographic figure and plot out numbered points.
(f) Form points to form a curve and repeat in the other quadrant.

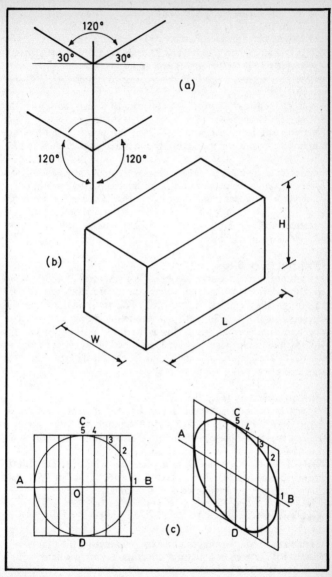

Figure 51

Method II (approximate arc)

(a) Draw the isometric square (Fig. 52a) in two planes.

(b) Join the diagonals.

(c) In the isometric square $ABCD$ draw horizontal lines from C and A to cut the diagonals in S and T.

(d) With centres S and T draw arcs to touch AB/BC and AD/DC.

(e) With centres A and C draw arcs to touch and join the two previous arcs.

Note In the isometric square $DCEF$, the points S_1 and T_1 are obtained by drawing lines at $60°$ to the horizontal from E and F.

Isometric drawing is not an absolutely true projection as it does not take into account any foreshortening that would occur in a pictorial presentation. An isometric scale can be produced (Fig. 52b), but little use is made of an isometric scale in practice, and it is customary to take the true or natural lengths along the isometric lines.

Oblique (Fig. 52c)

In oblique, one face of the object is presented at right-angles to the viewer, while the other faces are inclined at $45°$ (although they can be $30°$ or $60°$). The right-angled face will be seen as full size but all measurements along the $45°$ axes are half the normal size. This is to present the object in a well-proportioned visual view. Figure 52d shows a cube drawn with all faces equal in length and it can be clearly seen that this looks very 'un-cube' like.

Oblique circles (Fig. 52e)

Circles in oblique are best drawn by the ordinate method as for isometric circles (Fig. 51c). The diameter AB must however be half the normal size, although the **same** number of divisions must be used.

Note It would seem much more sensible wherever possible to draw oblique circles in the **front plane** as in Fig. 52e and this is certainly an advantage over an isometric view.

Key terms

Ordinate   Line parallel to one axis and meeting the other.
Pictorial   Drawn as a picture, effecting 3-dimensional.
Quadrant   Quarter of a circle.

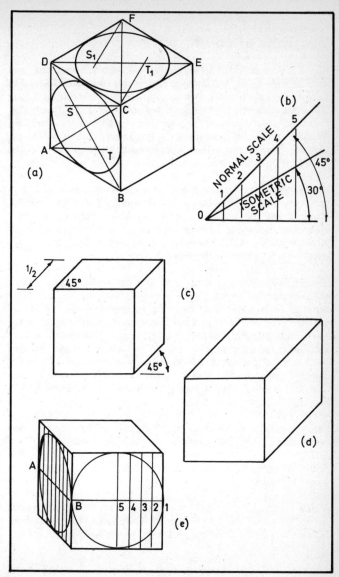

Figure 52

Chapter 14
Sections of solids

We have dealt with orthographic, auxiliary, isometric and oblique projection, but in each case so far only **outside** views have been drawn. In order to obtain even more information about an object it is sometimes necessary to cut through that object in a certain way. The cut lines are known as **cutting planes** and the exposed surface is known as a **section.** The cut surface of a section view is **cross-hatched** at 45° to the main outline of the object.

If the section is parallel to the planes of reference, then the section takes the place of the normal view as in Fig. 53a. However, if the section is an inclined one then an auxiliary view is necessary to give the section. Normally that auxiliary view would be at right-angles to the cutting plane and this would result in a **true-shape** (Fig. 53b).

The sections drawn of circular shapes are rather more difficult than sections of angular ones because the points on the curve have to be plotted as in Fig. 53c. In the plan the semi-circle has been divided up into 8 equal divisions and projected up to the cutting plane $a-a$. Lines from the equal division on the end view have also been projected to this cutting plane. Having established a new **centre line** O-O, the widths of the circle are stepped about it. The length of the line O-O is much greater than the original diameter of the cylinder although the widths are the same.

In the section of some solids (Figs. 54a and b) certain loci are produced, i.e., the parabola and the hyperbola.

Some drawings will show sections included within the elevation as in Fig. 55a and b.

Note Cross-hatching lines should be suitably and evenly spaced according to the area to be covered. They should be drawn more lightly than the bold outline and at 45° to the horizontal.

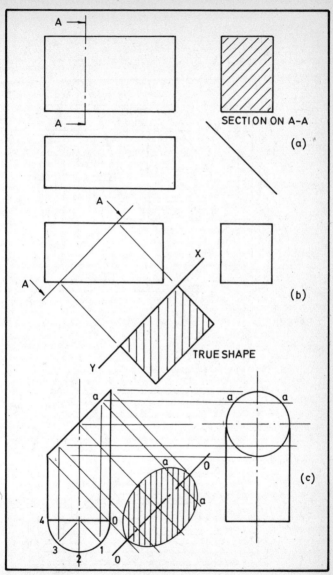

SECTION ON A-A

(a)

A

X

TRUE SHAPE

Y

(b)

a

a

a

a

a

a

4

0

0

0

3

1

2

(c)

Figure 53

111

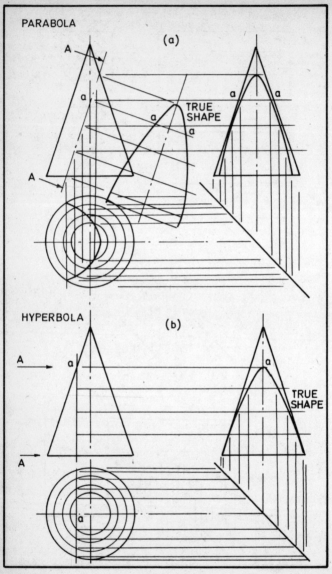

PARABOLA

(a)

A

a

a

a

TRUE SHAPE

A

a   a

HYPERBOLA

(b)

A   a

a

TRUE SHAPE

A

a

Figure 54

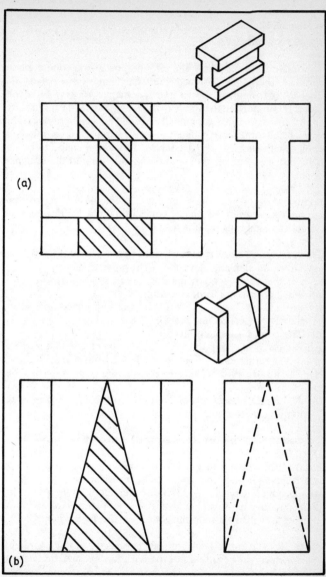

(a)

(b)

Figure 55

Chapter 15
Intersections

When two solid geometric shapes meet, or appear joined to one another, there is a contact line. This line is known as the **line of interpenetration** and the shapes are said to **intersect.** It is important to be able to draw or plot this line accurately, as in most cases development is needed in orthographic. This is especially the case when the orthographic views are concerned with sheet work. It enables the correct shape to be cut from flat sheet metal stock and then made up into the designed object.

Points are established upon the curve or line of interpenetration by taking a series of 'slices' or cutting planes through the object and analysing what is seen (Fig. 56a).

To construct the intersection of two pipes (Fig. 56b)
(a) Draw the plan and elevation of the pipes as shown.
(b) On the end elevation take a section $a-a$ and project this line across to the front elevation.
(c) Project the line $a-a$ down from the end elevation and via the 45° projection line draw lines to the plan.
(d) These lines will meet the plan in $a-a$.
(e) *Project $a-a$* from the plan to the front elevation to cut the lines that have already been drawn from $a-a$ in (b).
(f) The intersection of these lines gives the point a in the front elevation.
(g) A number of sections are required (at least eight) in order to plot a good curve.

To construct the intersection of a pipe to a cone (Fig. 56c)
Follow the same principles as for the previous construction but remember that the cone, as sections are cut through it, will produce circles of different diameters. When plotting your points you must be aware of the sections of the pipe altering as well as those of the cone. See also Figs. 57 and 58.

Note If a straight-sided object intersects another straight-sided object, the resulting interpenetration line will be straight-lined.

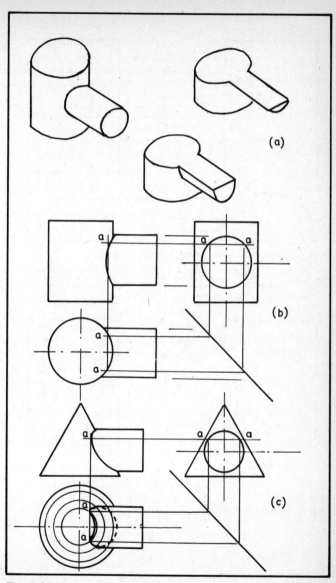

Figure 56

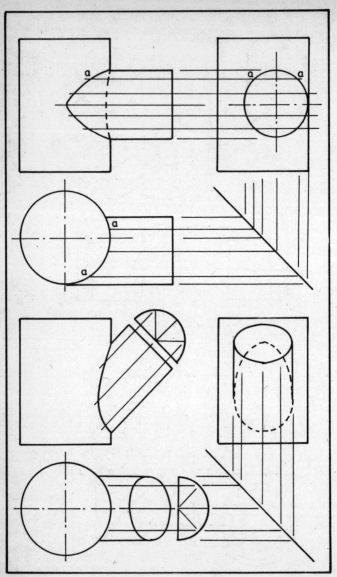

Figure 57

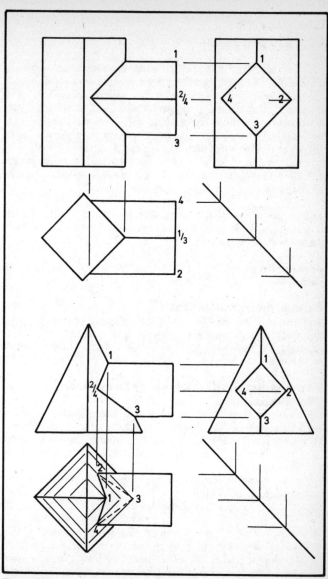

Figure 58

Chapter 16
Developments

In sheet metalwork many components are stamped out or are cut from a flat sheet of metal and then formed into some object. In order to be able to make this object accurately, it is necessary to calculate its shape by means of drawing the **development** of the three-dimensional component onto a two-dimensional material. A pattern or template can then be made and from this the sheet metalworker can produce as many copies as is required. An accurate and carefully worked out development will allow the manufacturer to cost his product and to economise on the number of pressings per sheet of material.

The shapes of most engineering components are whole or parts of pyramids, cones, prisms and cylinders. There are two main methods of development:

parallel line
radial line

Parallel line development
This method can only be used for developing objects having a uniform cross-section, e.g., prisms and cylinders. It can be used for a round-sided or straight-sided object either in whole or in part.

To construct the development of a cylinder
(Fig. 59a)
(a) Draw the given elevation and plan of the cylinder.
(b) Draw the base line AB equal in length to the circumference of the base circle. (This can be obtained by dividing the circle into at least eight equal units and numbering as shown.)
(c) It is **most** important to position the numbers for any plotting on any figure.
(d) $ABCD$ is the development of the cylinder.

If however a cut ST is made upon the cylinder as in Fig. 59b, it becomes necessary to project lines from that cut across the development area. This is achieved by projecting the intersections of the line ST with the **generators** projected up from the plan.

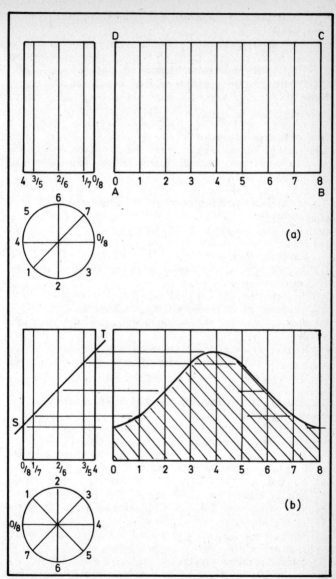

Figure 59

To construct the development of a hexagonal prism (Fig. 60a)

(a) The construction is very similar to that of the cylinder but in this case the base *AB* is more easily calculated as it is the sides of the prism 'stepped off' six times.

(b) The resulting development will have straight-sides.

Note Any 'cuts' upon the surface will be obtained in exactly the same way as in the previous example (Fig. 60b).

Radial line development

This method of development uses radial surface lines and is used for cones and pyramids, that is to say, shapes that have an apex and a base.

To construct the development of a right cone (Fig. 60c)

(a) Draw the given elevation and plan.

(b) Divide the plan into at least eight equal sections and number as shown.

(c) Project these points from the circumference to the base line of the front elevation *AB*.

(d) Project these points on the base *AB* to the apex at *C*.

(e) With centre *C* and radius *CB* draw an arc *BD*.

(f) Step off on this arc the eight equal divisions from the plan.

(g) Each division on this arc is drawn back to the apex at *C*.

(h) It is important to number correctly as shown.

(i) *BCD* is the development of the right cone.

To construct the development of the frustum of a cone (Fig. 60d)

(a) Set out the problem as in the previous construction.

(b) Draw the cutting line *ST* on the front elevation.

(c) The cutting line *ST* intersects the **generators** from the base line in the points *S*, *T*, and *X*, *Y*, *Z*.

(d) The distances *CX*, *CY* and *CZ* are **not** true lengths and can only be made so by projecting *X*, *Y* and *Z* to the outside lines of the cone *CB*, (in fact making them parallel to the vertical plane).

(e) The points are projected from the line *CB* onto the development area *CBD*.

(f) *S* and *T* are already on the outside lines *CA* and *CB*.

Note The developed area can be cross-hatched at 45° and clearly marked as shown.

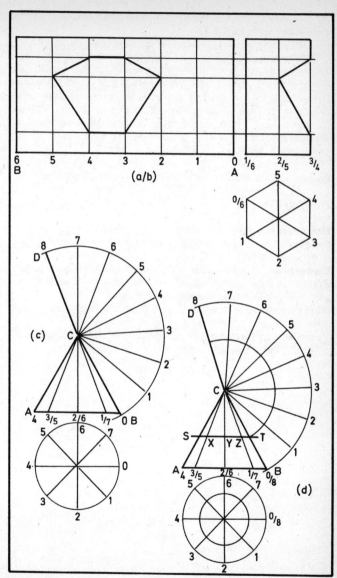

Figure 60

To construct the development of a hexagonal pyramid cut obliquely (Fig. 61a)

(a) Draw the plan and elevation of the hexagonal pyramid.

(b) Using previous knowledge lay out the development as shown.

Note The front elevation does not show the true length of a corner of the pyramid. The true length AB is found by making C_1 parallel to the vertical plane. The front elevation does not show the true distance from C to any of the corners and therefore these foreshortened distances have all to be projected horizontally across to the line AB before being used on the development area.

Figures 61b and 61c are further examples of development.

Key terms

Component One part of a machine or engine.

Frustum A cone truncated (chopped off) by a plane parallel to its base.

Generator Any line lying in the surface of a cone or cylinder.

Prism A solid object whose cross-section shape remains the same when it is cut at right-angles to its axis.

Right cone A cone whose vertex is directly over the centre of its base.

Template or pattern An outline around whose shape repeatedly identical shapes can be cut.

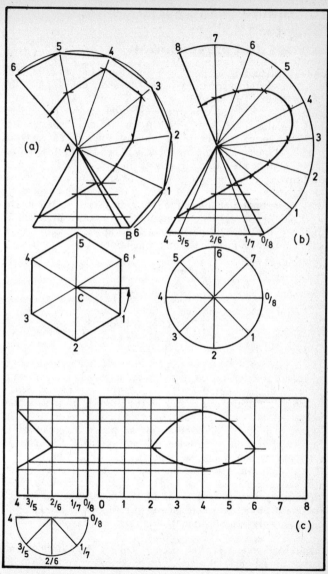

Figure 61

Section IV Technical Drawing
Chapter 17
Layout and presentation

Before attempting to draw any object orthographically, it is most important to try and visualise the shape and form of the object itself. To this end, it is well worth sketching on a piece of scrap paper your rough pictorial idea of the object. Five minutes spent doing this will pay dividends later, rather than attempting to draw 'blind' what is required. You may, of course, be given all the extra views you need and so the object itself is perfectly clear. If this is the case, then the next objective is to line up your paper in the standard way as shown in Fig. 62a. As I have said before, technical or engineering drawing is about communication. The more precise and clear your work and the neater its presentation, the more easily it will be understood. The title block should be at the bottom of the sheet and should include the following information:

> (a) Name
> (b) Date
> (c) Title
> (d) Scale ratio
> (e) Projection symbol
> (f) Drawing number

Having drawn the margin and the title block, the next step is to set out the drawing correctly on the paper. Two main points have to be considered at this stage; the size of the paper, and the size of the object that is to be drawn. In most school situations, A_2 cartridge paper is used and therefore it is the object that has to be sized to fit the paper. A scale has to be established and in order to conform to B.S. 308 it is likely to be stated on the paper as 1:1 or 2:1 or 1:2, etc. The overall dimensions of the object, that is the full length, width and height, are calculated and these measurements taken from the height and width of the drawing paper. There is no need to be too fussy, the whole idea is to position the orthographic views **evenly** spaced within the framework of the margin.

Figure 62b gives a typical spacing plan for three orthographic views in 1st-angle projection. The drawing appears to be 'balanced' and as a result, more attractive and acceptable.

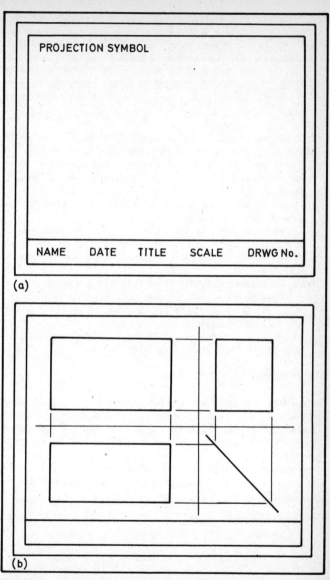

PROJECTION SYMBOL

NAME   DATE   TITLE   SCALE   DRWG No.

(a)

(b)

Figure 62

125

Valuable time and marks are often lost by students who have neglected to spend a few minutes on this initial calculation. They may find that they have 'run out' of paper or that their work appears squashed or totally unbalanced, or indeed that they have used an incorrect scale. This 'sizing' can quite easily be calculated on a piece of scrap paper and after a short time students can 'place' a drawing in a matter of moments.

All students should adopt a method of building up their drawing after the initial stages mentioned above.

(a) Use only light lines (4H pencil) until the final stages as any mistakes are more easily erased without spoiling the work.
(b) Draw centre lines within the framework already discussed in Fig. 62b and 63a.
(c) Locate and draw in all circles or parts of circles as it is so much easier to draw straight lines to circles rather than attempt to position circles or arcs onto a straight line (Fig. 63b).
(d) Position webs and other outline details (Fig. 64a).
(e) Add hidden details and any nuts and bolts (Fig. 64b).
(f) After checking the drawing carefully, it can be lined in using a 2H pencil (Fig. 65a).
(g) Finally, the drawing should be correctly dimensioned and the title block added (Fig. 65b).

Key terms

B.S. 308 Book issued by the British Standards Institution and recommended for engineering and technical drawing students.
Drawing number Each drawing that the student draws should have an identification number – purely for useful reference at a later date.
Projection symbol A quick method of stating whether the drawing is in 1st- or 3rd-angle projection. See list of abbreviations on page 135.

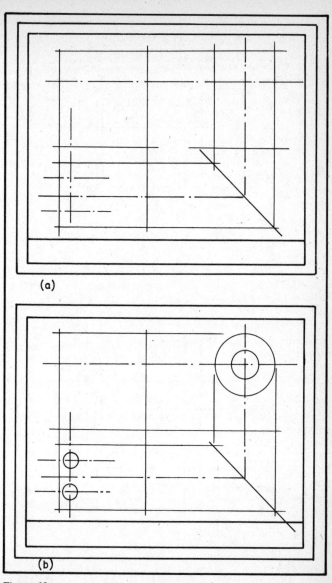

(a)

(b)

Figure 63

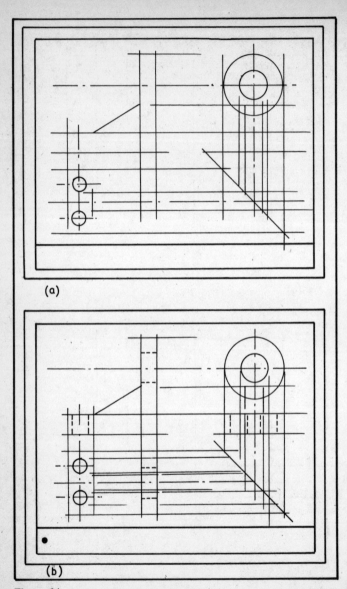

Figure 64

128

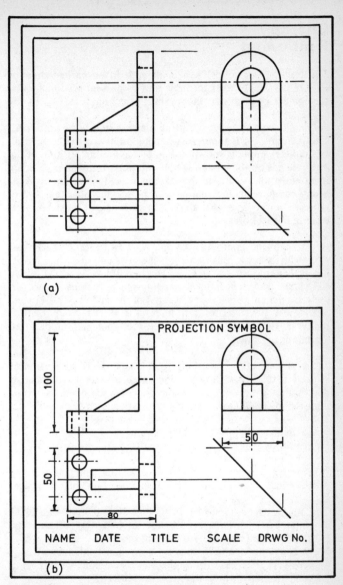

(a)

PROJECTION SYMBOL

100

50

80

50

NAME   DATE   TITLE   SCALE   DRWG No.

(b)

Figure 65

129

Chapter 18
Sectioning

The 'sections of solids' was dealt with in an earlier chapter. It is necessary however to know how to present sectional views of engineering parts in orthographic projection.

Any solid that is cut by a cutting plane is said to be sectioned. The resulting cut is then cross-hatched at 45° to the horizontal. A simple example is shown in Fig. 66a. Note the position of the arrow-heads on the end elevation pointing towards the sectional front elevation, and note the statement below, section on *A-A*. Many components are made up of more than one item and of more than one type of material. In each case it must be made clear in the sectioning.

In Fig. 66b the component is made of two pieces of say cast iron with a brass bush insert. The top and base are cross-hatched in opposite directions. The brass bush, which is in two halves, is also cross-hatched in opposite directions. However, the cross-hatching is closer than that of the main body. Hatched lines must never cross full lines, for if the component is really in two parts, the parts must be hatched in different directions as shown.

There are certain exceptions to the general rule. Sectioning is used to clarify a drawing and there are some engineering details that if sectioned lose their identity or create a wrong impression. The following items are never shown sectioned:

(a) Nuts and bolts   (f) Screws
(b) Studs   (g) Shafts
(c) Keys   (h) Webs
(d) Gear teeth   (i) Ball bearings and ball races
(e) Pins   (j) Roller bearings and roller races

To complicate matters even further, webs and shafts are **NOT** cross-hatched when cut longitudinally but **ARE** when cut laterally. Figures 66c and 66d show examples of this.
Note Hatch lines should never be more than 4 mm apart. It may be necessary to change the angle of cross-hatching when part of the main outline of the component is itself at 45°.

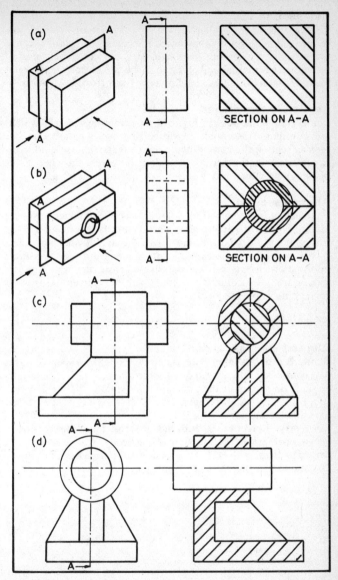

(a) SECTION ON A-A

(b) SECTION ON A-A

(c)

(d)

Figure 66

Half section

This type of section applies to components that are symmetrical in form. It is therefore considered unnecessary to show a complete sectional view but only half. It is also extremely useful that both the internal and external shape can be seen in the one view. Figure 67a is an example of a **half-sectional** elevation.

Section in two planes

The cutting plane *A-A* in Fig. 67b passes through details which are considered essential. In order that these details can be seen in section the cutting plane has changed 'course' and is in two planes. In the resulting section, however, the change of plane is now shown and the cross-hatching remains 'clear'.

Aligned section

This section is used when sectioning parts or components whose features lie on a **radial** line. The section is drawn as if *B-B* was on the principal centre line *A-A*. This avoids what would be a very awkward projection and at the same time gives useful information about the internal shape. Note that the ribs or spokes are not sectioned to comply with the convention (rules) concerning webs (Fig. 67c).

Key terms

Aligned Bring into line.

Brass bush An inner core generally made from special brass that is inserted into a component of less hard-wearing material. A shaft or axial will then remain true within this brass core. It is also much easier to replace the bush when worn rather than the entire component.

Laterally Refers to a section taken across the major axis of a web or shaft and **is** therefore cross-hatched.

Longitudinally Refers to a section cut parallel to the major axis and **is not** therefore cross-hatched.

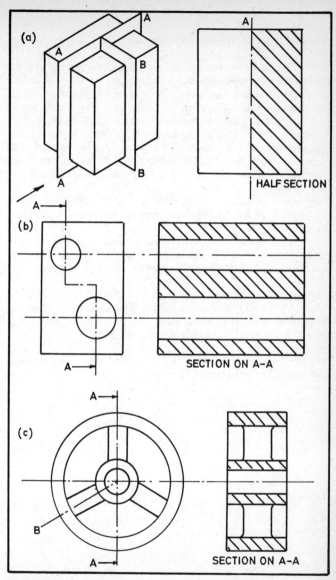

Figure 67

Chapter 19
Useful engineering data

The draughtsman is the middle man between designer and the skilled men whose job it is to actually make the article. Since designer and workman may never meet, it is essential for the draughtsman to convey the ideas and design in a totally accurate manner. The drawings he produces may well be 'read' by many people of different nationalities. Therefore engineering drawing must be standardised so that anyone familiar with these standards could manufacture the product. This international 'language' makes use of symbols, abbreviations and conventions.

The use of symbols, abbreviations and conventions saves time and space and allows the draughtsman to convey detail which might otherwise be difficult and tedius to draw. It is obviously much quicker and much less tedious to have a convention for a screw thread than to expect the draughtsman to spend unnecessary time on drawing the minute thread.

I have included in this chapter then, a number of data sheets which I hope will be of some help to the student draughtsman. The information is nowhere near conclusive but is more than adequate for the CSE or GCE O-level requirements.

British Standards 308 gives the rules for engineering drawing and should be carefully studied by every prospective draughtsman.

Abbreviations

A/F	Across flats	MATL	Material
Al.	Aluminium	MAX	Maximum
ASSY	Assembly	M.S.	Mild steel
Br.	Brass	MIN	Minimum
BS	British Standard	m	Metre
BSP	British Standard Pipe	mm	Millimetre
C.I.	Cast iron	NO.	Number
cm	Centimetre	O/D	Outside diameter
CRS	Centres	PATT	
CL or ℄	Centre line	NO.	Pattern number
CHAM	Chamfered	PCD	Pitch circle diameter
CH HD	Cheese head	PNEU	Pneumatic
Cpr	Copper	RAD	Radius
CSK	Countersunk	R	Radius
CSK HD	Countersunk head	REQD	Required
C'BORE	Counterbore	RH	Right-hand
CYL	Cylinder	RD HD	Round head
DIA	Diameter	SCR	Screwed
Ø	Diameter	SH	Sheet
DRG	Drawing	SI	Système
EXT	External		International
FIG.	Figure	SK	Sketch
	First-angle projection	SPEC	Specification
		SPHERE Ø	Spherical diameter
HEX	Hexagon		
HEX HD	Hexagon head	SPHERE R	Spherical radius
HYD	Hydraulic		
ISO	International Organization for Standardization	S'FACE	Spotface
		SQ	Square
		□	Square
(I)SWG	Imperial Standard Wire Gauge	STD	Standard
		TPI	Threads per inch
INSUL	Insulated		Third-angle projection
INT	Internal		
I/D	Internal diameter	U'CUT	Undercut
kg	Kilogram	UNC	Unified coarse
LH	Left-hand	UNF	Unified fine
LG	Long	UNS	Unified selected
M/C	Machine	VOL	Volume
M/CD	Machined	WT	Weight
M/CY	Machinery		

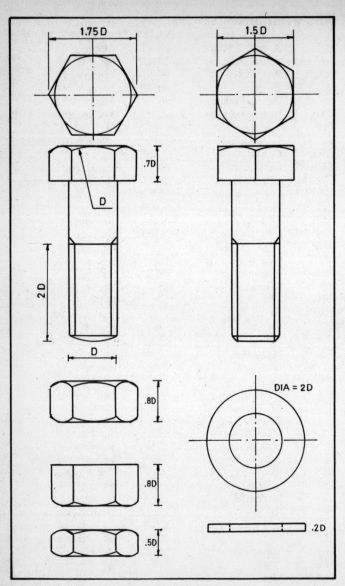

Figure 68

136

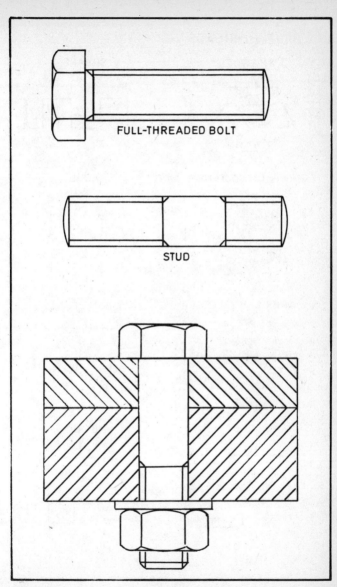

FULL-THREADED BOLT

STUD

Figure 69

137

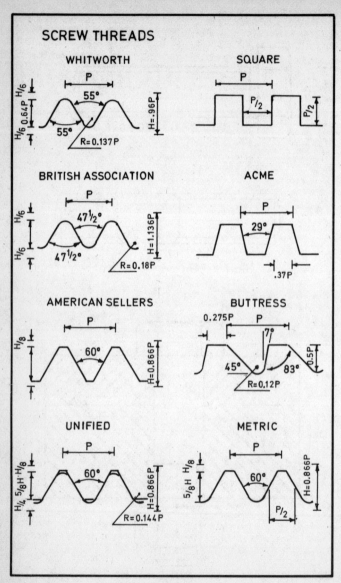

Figure 70

138

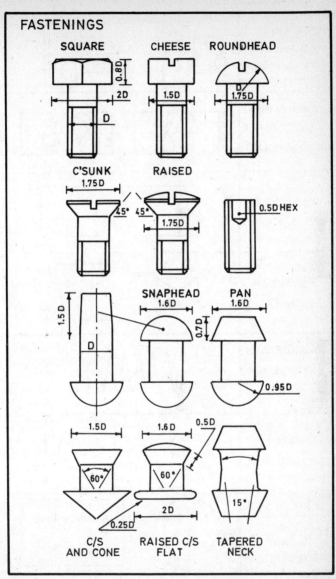

Figure 71

CONVENTIONS

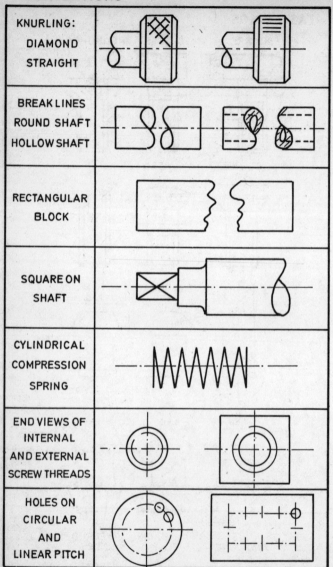

KNURLING: DIAMOND STRAIGHT	
BREAK LINES ROUND SHAFT HOLLOW SHAFT	
RECTANGULAR BLOCK	
SQUARE ON SHAFT	
CYLINDRICAL COMPRESSION SPRING	
END VIEWS OF INTERNAL AND EXTERNAL SCREW THREADS	
HOLES ON CIRCULAR AND LINEAR PITCH	

Figure 72

140

Metrication

International system of units

Length	= metre	= m	= (39.37 in)
Mass	= kilogram	= kg	= (2.2046 lb)
Time	= second	= sec	
Electrical	= ampere	= A	
Temp	= Kelvin	= K	
Luminous density	= candela	= cd	
Distance	= kilometre	= km	= (0.621 mile)
Speed		= km/hr	= (0.62 mph)
Weight	= metric tonne	= 1000 kg	
Capacity	= litre	= 1	= (1.76 pints)
Power	= kilowatt	= kw	= (1000 watts)
Temperature	= degree Celsius	= °C	

Length (linear)

1 millimetre mm	= 0.03937 in	1 in	= 25.4 mm
1 centimetre cm	= 0.3937 in	1 ft	= 30.48 cm
1 decimetre dm	= 3.937 in	1 yd	= 0.9288 m
1 metre m	= 39.37 in	1 mile	= 1.6 km
1 kilometre km	= 0.621 mile		

Square measure

1 sq. millimetre mm^2	= 0.00155 in^2	1 in^2	= 6.452 cm^2
1 sq. centimetre cm^2	= 0.155 in^2	1 yd^2	= 1.194 m^2
1 sq. metre m^2	= 10.764 ft^2		
1 sq. kilometre km^2	= 0.3861 $mile^2$		

Cubic measure (volume)

1 cubic millimetre	= mm^3	1 in^3	= 1 cubic inch
1 cubic centimetre	= cm^3	1 ft^3	= 1 cubic foot
1 cubic metre	= m^3	1 yd^3	= 1 cubic yard

Capacity (fluids)

Millilitre = ml		1 litre	= 61.025 in^2
Centilitre = cl			= 35.196 oz
Decilitre = dl			= 1.7598 pt
Litre = l	= 1000 cm^3		= 0.2199 gall

Weight (mass)

1 milligram = mg	= 0.0527 oz	1 oz	= 28.343 mg
1 kilogram = kg	= 35.274 oz = 2.2046 lb	1 lb	= 0.4535 kg

Conversion table inches to millimetres

inches	0.000	0.001	0.002	0.003	0.004	0.005	0.006	0.007	0.008	0.009
	millimetres									
0.000	–	0.0254	0.0508	0.0762	0.1016	0.1270	0.1524	0.1778	0.2032	0.2286
0.010	0.2540	0.2794	0.3048	0.3302	0.3556	0.3810	0.4064	0.4318	0.4572	0.4826
0.020	0.5080	0.5334	0.5588	0.5842	0.6096	0.6350	0.6604	0.6858	0.7112	0.7366
0.030	0.7620	0.7874	0.8128	0.8382	0.8636	0.8890	0.9144	0.9398	0.9652	0.9906
0.040	1.0160	1.0414	1.0668	1.0922	1.1176	1.1430	1.1684	1.1938	1.2192	1.2446
0.050	1.2700	1.2954	1.3208	1.3462	1.3716	1.3970	1.4224	1.4478	1.4732	1.4986
0.060	1.5240	1.5494	1.5748	1.6002	1.6256	1.6510	1.6764	1.7018	1.7272	1.7526
0.070	1.7780	1.8034	1.8288	1.8542	1.8796	1.9050	1.9304	1.9558	1.9812	2.0066
0.080	2.0320	2.0574	2.0828	2.1082	2.1336	2.1590	2.1844	2.2098	2.2352	2.2606
0.090	2.2860	2.3114	2.3368	2.3622	2.3876	2.4130	2.4384	2.4638	2.4892	2.5146
0.100	2.5400	2.5654	2.5908	2.6162	2.6416	2.6670	2.6924	2.7178	2.7432	2.7686
0.110	2.7940	2.8194	2.8448	2.8702	2.8956	2.9210	2.9464	2.9718	2.9972	3.0226
0.120	3.0480	3.0734	3.0988	3.1242	3.1496	3.1750	3.2004	3.2258	3.2512	3.2766
0.130	3.3020	3.3274	3.3528	3.3782	3.4036	3.4290	3.4544	3.4798	3.5052	3.5306
0.140	3.5560	3.5814	3.6068	3.6322	3.6576	3.6830	3.7084	3.7338	3.7592	3.7846
0.150	3.8100	3.8354	3.8608	3.8862	3.9116	3.9370	3.9624	3.9878	4.0132	4.0386
0.160	4.0640	4.0894	4.1148	4.1402	4.1656	4.1910	4.2164	4.2418	4.2672	4.2926
0.170	4.3180	4.3434	4.3688	4.3942	4.4196	4.4450	4.4704	4.4958	4.5212	4.5466
0.180	4.5720	4.5974	4.6228	4.6482	4.6736	4.6990	4.7244	4.7498	4.7752	4.8006
0.190	4.8260	4.8514	4.8768	4.9022	4.9276	4.9530	4.9784	5.0038	5.0292	5.0546
0.200	5.0800	5.1054	5.1308	5.1562	5.1816	5.2070	5.2324	5.2578	5.2832	5.3086
0.210	5.3340	5.3594	5.3848	5.4102	5.4356	5.4610	5.4864	5.5118	5.5372	5.5626
0.220	5.5880	5.6134	5.6388	5.6642	5.6896	5.7150	5.7404	5.7658	5.7912	5.8166
0.230	5.8420	5.8674	5.8928	5.9182	5.9436	5.9690	5.9944	6.0198	6.0452	6.0706
0.240	6.0960	6.1214	6.1468	6.1722	6.1976	6.2230	6.2484	6.2738	6.2992	6.3246
0.250	6.3500	6.3754	6.4008	6.4262	6.4516	6.4770	6.5024	6.5278	6.5532	6.5786
0.260	6.6040	6.6294	6.6548	6.6802	6.7056	6.7310	6.7564	6.7818	6.8072	6.8326
0.270	6.8580	6.8834	6.9088	6.9342	6.9596	6.9850	7.0104	7.0358	7.0612	7.0866
0.280	7.1120	7.1374	7.1628	7.1882	7.2136	7.2390	7.2644	7.2898	7.3152	7.3406
0.290	7.3660	7.3914	7.4168	7.4422	7.4676	7.4930	7.5184	7.5438	7.5692	7.5946
0.300	7.6200	7.6454	7.6708	7.6962	7.7216	7.7470	7.7724	7.7978	7.8232	7.8486
0.310	7.8740	7.8994	7.9248	7.9502	7.9756	8.0010	8.0264	8.0518	8.0772	8.1026
0.320	8.1280	8.1534	8.1788	8.2042	8.2296	8.2550	8.2804	8.3058	8.3312	8.3566
0.330	8.3820	8.4074	8.4328	8.4582	8.4836	8.5090	8.5344	8.5598	8.5852	8.6106
0.340	8.6360	8.6614	8.6868	8.7122	8.7376	8.7630	8.7884	8.8138	8.8392	8.8646
0.350	8.8900	8.9154	8.9408	8.9662	8.9916	9.0170	9.0424	9.0678	9.0932	9.1186
0.360	9.1440	9.1694	9.1948	9.2202	9.2456	9.2710	9.2964	9.3218	9.3472	9.3726
0.370	9.3980	9.4234	9.4488	9.4742	9.4996	9.5250	9.5504	9.5758	9.6012	9.6266
0.380	9.6520	9.6774	9.7028	9.7282	9.7536	9.7790	9.8044	9.8298	9.8552	9.8806
0.390	9.9060	9.9314	9.9568	9.9822	10.0076	10.0330	10.0584	10.0838	10.1092	10.1346
0.400	10.1600	10.1854	10.2108	10.2362	10.2616	10.2870	10.3124	10.3378	10.3632	10.3886
0.410	10.4140	10.4394	10.4648	10.4902	10.5156	10.5410	10.5664	10.5918	10.6172	10.6426
0.420	10.6680	10.6934	10.7188	10.7442	10.7696	10.7950	10.8204	10.8458	10.8712	10.8966
0.430	10.9220	10.9474	10.9728	10.9982	11.0236	11.0490	11.0744	11.0998	11.1252	11.1506
0.440	11.1760	11.2014	11.2268	11.2522	11.2776	11.3030	11.3284	11.3538	11.3792	11.4046
0.450	11.4300	11.4554	11.4808	11.5062	11.5316	11.5570	11.5824	11.6078	11.6332	11.6586
0.460	11.6840	11.7094	11.7348	11.7602	11.7856	11.8110	11.8364	11.8618	11.8872	11.9126
0.470	11.9380	11.9634	11.9888	12.0142	12.0396	12.0650	12.0904	12.1158	12.1412	12.1666
0.480	12.1920	12.2174	12.2428	12.2682	12.2936	12.3190	12.3444	12.3698	12.3952	12.4206
0.490	12.4460	12.4714	12.4968	12.5222	12.5476	12.5730	12.5984	12.6238	12.6492	12.6746

Conversion table inches to millimetres

.500" to 1.000" in increments of .001"

inches	0.000	0.001	0.002	0.003	0.004	0.005	0.006	0.007	0.008	0.009
	millimetres									
0.500	12.7000	12.7254	12.7508	12.7762	12.8016	12.8270	12.8524	12.8778	12.9032	12.9286
0.510	12.9540	12.9794	13.0048	13.0302	13.0556	13.0810	13.1064	13.1318	13.1572	13.1826
0.520	13.2080	13.2334	13.2588	13.2842	13.3096	13.3350	13.3604	13.3858	13.4112	13.4366
0.530	13.4620	13.4874	13.5128	13.5382	13.5636	13.5890	13.6144	13.6398	13.6652	13.6906
0.540	13.7160	13.7414	13.7668	13.7922	13.8176	13.8430	13.8684	13.8938	13.9192	13.9446
0.550	13.9700	13.9954	14.0208	14.0462	14.0716	14.0970	14.1224	14.1478	14.1732	14.1986
0.560	14.2240	14.2494	14.2748	14.3002	14.3256	14.3510	14.3764	14.4018	14.4272	14.4526
0.570	14.4780	14.5034	14.5288	14.5542	14.5796	14.6050	14.6304	14.6558	14.6812	14.7066
0.580	14.7320	14.7574	14.7828	14.8082	14.8336	14.8590	14.8844	14.9098	14.9352	14.9606
0.590	14.9860	15.0114	15.0368	15.0622	15.0876	15.1130	15.1384	15.1638	15.1892	15.2146
0.600	15.2400	15.2654	15.2908	15.3162	15.3416	15.3670	15.3924	15.4178	15.4432	15.4686
0.610	15.4940	15.5194	15.5448	15.5702	15.5956	15.6210	15.6464	15.6718	15.6972	15.7226
0.620	15.7480	15.7734	15.7988	15.8242	15.8496	15.8750	15.9004	15.9258	15.9512	15.9766
0.630	16.0020	16.0274	16.0528	16.0782	16.1036	16.1290	16.1544	16.1798	16.2052	16.2306
0.640	16.2560	16.2814	16.3068	16.3322	16.3576	16.3830	16.4084	16.4338	16.4592	16.4846
0.650	16.5100	16.5354	16.5608	16.5862	16.6116	16.6370	16.6624	16.6878	16.7132	16.7386
0.660	16.7640	16.7894	16.8148	16.8402	16.8656	16.8910	16.9164	16.9418	16.9672	16.9926
0.670	17.0180	17.0434	17.0688	17.0942	17.1196	17.1450	17.1704	17.1958	17.2212	17.2466
0.680	17.2720	17.2974	17.3228	17.3482	17.3736	17.3990	17.4244	17.4498	17.4752	17.5006
0.690	17.5260	17.5514	17.5768	17.6022	17.6276	17.6530	17.6784	17.7038	17.7292	17.7546
0.700	17.7800	17.8054	17.8308	17.8562	17.8816	17.9070	17.9324	17.9578	17.9832	18.0086
0.710	18.0340	18.0594	18.0848	18.1102	18.1356	18.1610	18.1864	18.2118	18.2372	18.2626
0.720	18.2880	18.3134	18.3388	18.3642	18.3896	18.4150	18.4404	18.4658	18.4912	18.5166
0.730	18.5420	18.5674	18.5928	18.6182	18.6436	18.6690	18.6944	18.7198	18.7452	18.7706
0.740	18.7960	18.8214	18.8468	18.8722	18.8976	18.9230	18.9484	18.9738	18.9992	19.0246
0.750	19.0500	19.0754	19.1008	19.1262	19.1516	19.1770	19.2024	19.2278	19.2532	19.2786
0.760	19.3040	19.3294	19.3548	19.3802	19.4056	19.4310	19.4564	19.4818	19.5072	19.5326
0.770	19.5580	19.5834	19.6088	19.6342	19.6596	19.6850	19.7104	19.7358	19.7612	19.7866
0.780	19.8120	19.8374	19.8628	19.8882	19.9136	19.9390	19.9644	19.9898	20.0152	20.0406
0.790	20.0660	20.0914	20.1168	20.1422	20.1676	20.1930	20.2184	20.2438	20.2692	20.2946
0.800	20.3200	20.3454	20.3708	20.3962	20.4216	20.4470	20.4724	20.4978	20.5232	20.5486
0.810	20.5740	20.5994	20.6248	20.6502	20.6756	20.7010	20.7264	20.7518	20.7772	20.8026
0.820	20.8280	20.8534	20.8788	20.9042	20.9296	20.9550	20.9804	21.0058	21.0312	21.0566
0.830	21.0820	21.1074	21.1328	21.1582	21.1836	21.2090	21.2344	21.2598	21.2852	21.3106
0.840	21.3360	21.3614	21.3868	21.4122	21.4376	21.4630	21.4884	21.5138	21.5392	21.5646
0.850	21.5900	21.6154	21.6408	21.6662	21.6916	21.7170	21.7424	21.7678	21.7932	21.8186
0.860	21.8440	21.8694	21.8948	21.9202	21.9456	21.9710	21.9964	22.0218	22.0472	22.0726
0.870	22.0980	22.1234	22.1488	22.1742	22.1996	22.2250	22.2504	22.2758	22.3012	22.3266
0.880	22.3520	22.3774	22.4028	22.4282	22.4536	22.4790	22.5044	22.5298	22.5552	22.5806
0.890	22.6060	22.6314	22.6568	22.6822	22.7076	22.7330	22.7584	22.7838	22.8092	22.8346
0.900	22.8600	22.8854	22.9108	22.9362	22.9616	22.9870	23.0124	23.0378	23.0632	23.0886
0.910	23.1140	23.1394	23.1648	23.1902	23.2156	23.2410	23.2664	23.2918	23.3172	23.3426
0.920	23.3680	23.3934	23.4188	23.4442	23.4696	23.4950	23.5204	23.5458	23.5712	23.5966
0.930	23.6220	23.6474	23.6728	23.6982	23.7236	23.7490	23.7744	23.7998	23.8252	23.8506
0.940	23.8760	23.9014	23.9268	23.9522	23.9776	24.0030	24.0284	24.0538	24.0792	24.1046
0.950	24.1300	24.1554	24.1808	24.2062	24.2316	24.2570	24.2824	24.3078	24.3332	24.3586
0.960	24.3840	24.4094	24.4348	24.4602	24.4856	24.5110	24.5364	24.5618	24.5872	24.6126
0.970	24.6380	24.6634	24.6888	24.7142	24.7396	24.7650	24.7904	24.8158	24.8412	24.8666
0.980	24.8920	24.9174	24.9428	24.9682	24.9936	25.0190	25.0444	25.0698	25.0952	25.1206
0.990	25.1460	25.1714	25.1968	25.2222	25.2476	25.2730	25.2984	25.3238	25.3492	25.3746
1.000	25.4000	—	—	—	—	—	—	—	—	—

143

Chapter 20
Examination questions

This chapter has been included so that the student can practice answering typical examination questions. It is hoped that by using the preceding chapters sensibly to back up or reinforce knowledge, the student will gain confidence in answering any questions.

The questions have been grouped in the same order as the chapters.

Lines and angles

1. Draw circles of 75 mm diameter and within those circles draw the following:
segments, chord, diameter, radius, quadrant, tangent, normal, sector, circumference.

2. Using only a compass draw angles of $80°$, $45°$, $27\frac{1}{2}°$, $60°$ and $15°$.

3. Draw a line 93 mm long. Divide it into 7 equal parts.

4. A line AB is 223 mm long, The line is divided in the ratio of $9:11:13$. Draw the line.

5. Draw a fourth proportional to three lines. Line $A = 20$ mm, line $B = 25$ mm and line $C = 45$ mm.

6. Draw the third proportional to two lines. Line $A = 47$ mm and line $B = 63$ mm.

7. Using compasses only, construct angles of $105°$, $135°$ and $120°$.

8. Draw a line AB, 50 mm long. Produce it to a point C so that $AB:AC = 3:7$.

9. Two paths meet at $45°$ and at the point of meeting, two walkers, A and B, start, one along each path. A travels at 65 metres per minute and B travels at 80 metres per minute. When B has walked 1000 metres how far has A walked?

Scales

1. Construct a diagonal scale in which 40 mm represents 1 m. The scale is to read down to 10 mm and is to cover a range of 6 m. Mark off a distance of 5 m 690 mm.

2. Construct a diagonal scale, ten times full size, to show mm and tenths of a mm and to read up to a maximum of 25 mm. Using this scale construct a triangle with sides of 19.8 mm, 15.6 mm and 12.2 mm.

3. Construct a plain scale of 60 mm = 600 mm to read to 10 mm up to 1200 mm. Using this scale draw a triangle having a perimeter of 1000 mm and having its sides in the ratio of 7:5:3.

4. Construct a scale of 30 mm = 1 km to read up to 6 km in divisions of 10 m. Show on this scale measurements of 2.64 km, 3.67 km and 5.79 km.

5. Construct a scale of 1 in 2.5 to measure up to 400 mm in mm. Measure on this scale 129 mm, 237 mm and 362 mm.

6. Construct a scale of 50 mm to 1 km to read up to 3 km in intervals of 100m. Measure on this scale a distance of 2.5 km, 1.3 km and 0.9 km.

7. Construct a diagonal scale of 25 mm to represent 1 m which can be used to measure in metres and 10 mm up to a maximum distance of 9 m. Using this scale construct a quadrilateral $ABCD$ which stands on a base AB of length 4 m 630 mm and having $BC = 3$ m 370 mm, $AD = 4$ m 270 mm, the angle $ABC = 110°$ and $ADC = 90°$.

8. It is necessary to make a drawing to a scale of 3:7. Construct a diagonal scale for this purpose to read in mm up to 350 mm.

9. A diagram has to be redrawn 2.5 times full size. Construct a diagonal scale which will read to millimetres for use in making this new drawing. Construct with this scale a triangle ABC such that $AB = 43$ mm, $BC = 34$ mm and $CD = 27$ mm.

10. The distance between two towns on a map of unknown scale measures 125 mm. If the actual distance between the towns is 25 km draw a diagonal scale suitable for the map.

Triangles

1. Construct a triangle of which the perimeter is 200 mm and of which two of the angles are 45° and 75°.

2. In the triangle ABC, $AB=70$ mm, $BC=95$ mm and $CA=55$ mm. In a circle of 60 mm inscribe a triangle similar to ABC.

3. In the triangle ABC, $AB=90$ mm, $BC=95$ mm and $CA=45$ mm. Inscribe in the triangle a square of which one side lies in AB.

4. A triangle has two sides in the ratio of 5:6 and an angle of 95°. Draw the triangle when the altitude is 55 mm.

5. In the triangle ABC, the side $AB=90$ mm, $BC=75$ mm and $CD=60$ mm. Divide the triangle into three equal areas by lines radiating from A.

6. An equilateral triangle has a side of 80 mm. Draw the triangle and then draw the two largest equal circles that can be placed inside it.

7. Draw a triangle that has a base of 65 mm and an opposite angle of 60°.

8. The perimeter of a triangle is 200 mm long. The sides are in the proportion of 7:5:3. Construct the triangle with the shortest side acting as base.

9. Construct the triangle ABC in which the base $BC=95$ mm, the vertex angle $A=65°$ and the altitude is 70 mm. D is a point on AB, 36 mm from A. Draw a circle to pass through the points A and D and which is tangential to the line BC.

10. Construct an isosceles triangle with equal sides 65 mm long and a vertical angle of 30°. On the same base describe another isosceles triangle with the vertical angle double that of the first triangle.

11. Draw the triangle ABC. The base $AC=50$ mm and the altitude is 45 mm. The angle $BAC=60°$.

12. Draw the circumscribing circle to a triangle ABC when $BC=70$ mm, angle $ABC=40°$ and the perimeter $=180$ mm.

Quadrilaterals

1. Draw a rhombus whose sides are 45 mm long and with one diagonal 75 mm long.

2. Construct a rectangle having a diagonal of 90 mm and a side of 40 mm.

3. Construct a parallelogram having adjacent sides of 75 mm and 50 mm respectively and an included angle of 60°.

4. Draw a quadrilateral given that $AB = 50$ mm, $BD = 60$ mm, $CD = 55$ mm, $AC = 75$ mm and the angle $ABC = 67\frac{1}{2}°$. Do not use a protractor.

5. Draw a quadrilateral given that $AB = 50$ mm, $BC = 42$ mm, $CD = 70$ mm and $DA = 57$ mm. The diagonal AC is at 30° to AB.

6. In the quadrilateral $ABCD$, $AB = 75$ mm, $BC = 95$ mm, $CD = 130$ mm, $DA = 72$ mm and the angle $DAB = 129°$. Divide the quadrilateral into two equal parts by a line passing through A.

7. A trapezium has an axis of 65 mm. If the diagonal is 45 mm in length and divides the axis in the ratio of 1:3 draw the figure.

8. Construct a trapezium given that the parallel sides are 50 mm and 80 mm long and are 45 mm apart.

9. The adjacent sides of a quadrilateral are 46 mm and 36 mm long respectively. The included angle is 60°. The other sides are 55 mm and 60 mm. Construct the figure.

10. The diagonals of a parallelogram are 50 mm and 65 mm long respectively. They intersect at an angle of 70°. Draw the figure without the use of a protractor.

11. Construct the quadrilateral $ABCD$ given that $AB = 85$ mm, $BC = 30$ mm, $CD = 30$ mm, $DA = 75$ mm and $BD = 45$ mm. The angle BCD is a re-entrant angle.

12. Draw the quadrilateral $ABCD$. The base $AD = 45$ mm, the angle at $A = 100°$ and the angle at $D = 120°$. The diagonal $AC = 82$ mm and the diagonal $BD = 60$ mm.

Polygons

1. Describe a regular octagon in a circle of 100 mm diameter.

2. Construct a polygon $ABCDE$ given that $AB = 58$ mm, $BC = 64$ mm, $CD = 75$ mm, $DE = 72$ mm. The angles $ABC = 120°$, $BCD = 100°$ and $CDE = 90°$.

3. Construct a regular pentagon, each side being 75 mm long.

4. Construct a regular octagon of side 75 mm and within this figure describe eight equal circles each touching one side of the octagon and the two adjacent circles. Draw the smallest circle which will touch all eight circles.

5. Inscribe a regular pentagon in a circle of 80 mm diameter.

6. Construct a regular hexagon given 65 mm across the flats.

7. A piece of wire 250 mm long is to be bent into the shape of a regular heptagon. Construct the figure.

8. Construct a pentagon given that $AB = BC = CD = 50$ mm. The diagonals $BE = CE = 75$ mm and the angles $EAB = EDC = 110°$.

9. Draw a regular polygon given that the angle subtended from its centre to one side is $40°$ and that the side is 25 mm.

10. Draw a regular decagon that has an inscribed circle of 60 mm.

11. Construct a regular pentagon $ABCDE$ given that the sides AB, BC, etc., are 75 mm long. Join AC and along AC make $AG = 100$ mm. Join AD and along AD make $AH = 100$ mm. Join GH and complete the regular pentagon $AFGHJ$ with sides equal to GH.

12. Construct a polygon $ABCDE$ given that $AB = 30$ mm, $BC = 38$ mm, $CD = 56$ mm, $DE = 30$ mm, $EA = 50$ mm and the diagonals $AC = 58$ mm and $AD = 70$ mm. Draw the circumscribing circle of this polygon and within the same circle construct a regular pentagon $PQRST$.

13. Construct a polygon $ABCDE$ from the following data: sides $AB = 60$ mm, $BC = 60$ mm, $CD = 45$ mm, $DE = 30$ mm, $AE = 35$ mm. The diagonals $AD = 50$ mm and $AC = 60$ mm.

Circles and tangents

1. Two circles have diameters of 80 mm and 30 mm and their centres are 100 mm apart. Construct the internal common tangent to the two circles.

2. The straight lines BA and BCD are inclined at 45°, $BC =$ 50 mm and $CD = 35$ mm. Construct the smaller circle which passes through C and D and touches BA.

3. OA and OB are two straight lines meeting at an angle of 30°. Construct a circle of 75 mm diameter to touch these two lines, and a smaller circle which will touch the two converging lines and the first circle.

4. ABC is a triangle in which $AB = 45$ mm, $BC = 80$ mm and $AC = 100$ mm. A is the centre of a circle of 35 mm diameter, B is the centre of a circle of 30 mm diameter and C is the centre of a 75 mm diameter circle.
Construct the figure and find the centre of the circle which circumscribes circles A, B and C.

5. A line AB is 125 mm long. Point A is the centre of a circle of 55 mm radius. Construct the tangents from point B to the circle.
Draw a smaller circle to touch the tangential lines from B and the circle A.

6. Construct a rhombus $ABCD$ given that $AB = 75$ mm and $AC = 130$ mm. With centre A and radius 75 mm describe the arc BD. Construct one circle to touch AB, AD and the arc BD, and another circle to touch BC, CD and the arc BD.

7. A segment of a circle stands on a chord AB which equals 50 mm. The angle in the segment is 55°. Draw the segment. Extend the chord AB to C so that $BC = 56$ mm. From C construct a tangent to the arc of the segment.

8. A triangle has sides of 100 mm, 105 mm and 50 mm. Draw the triangle and construct the inscribed circle, the circumscribed circle and the smaller escribed circle.

9. Describe three circles, each one touching the other two externally, their radii being, 15 mm, 20 mm and 25 mm.

Equal areas and similar figures

1. In the triangle ABC, $AB = 80$ mm, $BC = 105$ mm and $CA = 70$ mm. Draw a triangle similar to ABC but with area $1/5$th of ABC.

2. A square has a side of 45 mm. Construct a rectangle which is equal in area to the square and has one side of 60 mm.

3. Construct a square having its area equal to that of an equilateral triangle of side 100 mm. Construct a second square having its area equal to twice that of the first square.

4. Draw a quadrilateral $ABCD$ given that $AB = 75$ mm, $BC = 60$ mm, $CD = 100$ mm and $DA = 70$ mm. The angle $DAB = 100°$. Reduce the figure to a triangle of equal area.

5. Construct the polygon $ABCDE$ such that the base $AB = 95$ mm, $BC = 75$ mm, $CD = 55$ mm and $AE = 68$ mm. The angles $ABC = 120°$, $EAB = 82°$ and $CDE = 90°$. Construct a similar polygon but with $AB = 118$ mm.

6. Three squares have side lengths of 30 mm, 40 mm and 55 mm respectively. Construct a single square whose area is equal to the sum of the three squares.

7. Construct a triangle ABC given that $AB = 90$ mm, $BC = 75$ mm and $CA = 80$ mm. Construct a triangle CDA in which CD and CB are in the ratio of 5:7.

8. Construct a regular pentagon of side 55 mm. Construct a similar pentagon with sides $4/7$ths the length of the given figure.

9. Construct a triangle ABC given that $AB = 105$ mm, $BC = 80$ mm and $AC = 60$ mm. Divide the triangle into two parts by a line DE parallel to AB such that the area CDE is three times the area of $ABED$.

10. Construct a trapezium having its parallel sides of 125 mm and 55 mm respectively; the perpendicular distance between them is 50 mm and one diagonal is of length 105 mm. Construct a square equal in area to that of the trapezium.

11. In the triangle ABC, $AB = 50$ mm, $BC = 75$ mm and $CA = 65$ mm. Reduce the triangle to a square of equal area.

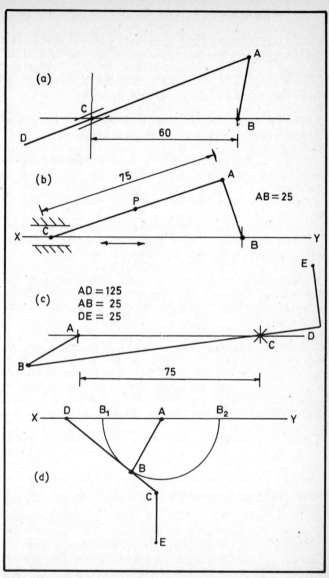

(a)

D ⎯⎯⎯ C ⎯⎯⎯ B
60

(b)

75
P
AB = 25
X ⎯⎯ C ⎯⎯⎯ A ⎯⎯ B ⎯⎯ Y

(c)

AD = 125
AB = 25
DE = 25

A
B
C D
E
75

(d)

X ⎯⎯ D ⎯ B₁ ⎯ A ⎯ B₂ ⎯ Y
B
C
E

Figure 73

151

Loci mechanisms

1. Two links AB and BC are connected by a pin-joint at P. The link AB rotates about a fixed centre O, whilst the end C of the other link is constrained to travel along a straight line passing through A. If $A = 38$ mm and $BC = 100$ mm draw the locus of the mid-point S of BC for one complete revolution of AB.

2. With a permanent base of 90 mm draw the locus of the vertices of all the triangles with a constant perimeter of 250 mm.

3. In the mechanism shown in Fig. 73a the crank AB rotates about B. The link AD passes through a slide which is free to pivot about C.
If $AB = 25$ mm and $AD = 100$ mm, plot the locus of D.

4. Figure 73b gives a simple crank-connecting rod mechanism. Plot the locus of the mid-point P of AC as the crank AB makes one revolution about B. C is constrained to move along XY.

5. Figure 73c shows a crank AB which rotates about B. The link AD passes through the slide pivoted at C. DE is attached at right-angles to AD. Plot the locus of E for one complete revolution of AB.

6. A simple mechanism is shown in Fig. 73d. The links ABC and D are pin-joints. The position of A is fixed. D can move in a horizontal direction along the line XY. The link CE is heavy and therefore always remains vertical. Plot the locus of a point F as AB moves from AB_1 to AB_2, given that $AB = 50$ mm, $BC = 25$ mm, $BD = 70$ mm and $CE = 40$ mm.

7. Figure 74a shows two links AD and BC which are free to rotate about the fixed points A and B respectively. Both links start from a horizontal position and swing up and outwards. The link AD rotates twice as quickly as the link BC. Plot the locus of the point of intersection E as the link AD moves through $90°$.

8. In the link mechanism in Fig. 74b, $AC = BD = 145$ mm, $BE = 70$ mm, $EF = 80$ mm, $AB = CD = EP = 25$ mm. AB and CD rotate about A and C respectively. F is constrained to move along the line XY. XY is at right-angles to AC and $AY = 40$ mm. Construct the locus of the point P when D completes one revolution.

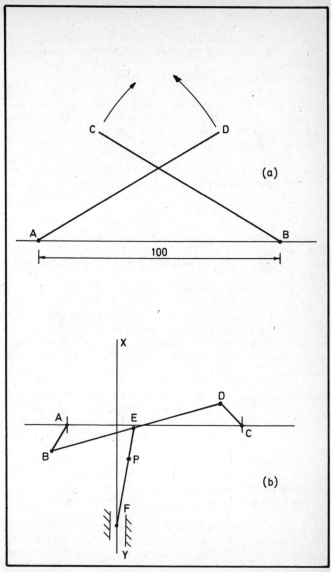

Figure 74

153

Ellipse

1. The major and minor axes of an ellipse are 125 mm and 80 mm respectively. Construct the ellipse and determine the position of the foci.
Draw the tangent to a point *P* on the curve.

2. Half the major axis of an ellipse is 75 mm long and half the minor axis is 45 mm. Construct one quarter of the ellipse and from a point 50 mm from each end of the axes construct tangents to the ellipse.

3. An ellipse has a major axis 150 mm long and its foci are 100 mm apart. Construct the ellipse. Draw the tangent and normal to the ellipse at a point *P* on the ellipse which is 55 mm distant from the intersection of the two axes.

4. A semi-ellipse has a major axis *AB* = 150 mm and a semi-minor axis *CD* = 60 mm. A line *EF*, 75 mm long, moves so that end *E* is always on the major axis and end *F* is always on the elliptical curve.
Draw the locus of the mid-point of *EF*.

5. Draw an ellipse having a major axis of 100 mm and a minor axis of 75 mm, having different constructions for the top and bottom halves. Construct a tangent to the ellipse from a point on the major axis extended and 95 mm from the centre of the ellipse.

6. A swimming pool is to be made in the shape of an ellipse. The overall dimensions of the pool are 20 metres by 8 metres. Draw a plan of the pool stating the working scale that you have used.

7. Construct a semi-ellipse having a major axis of 125 mm and a minor axis of 80 mm. Mark a point *P* on the ellipse measured on a straight line 30 mm from one end of the major axis. Draw a circle of 50 mm diameter to touch the ellipse at point *P*.

8. A masonry arch is to be made in the shape of a semi-ellipse. The maximum span of the arch is 3 metres and the height of the arch at the centre is 1 metre. The arch stands over a doorway that is 3 metres × 2 metres. Draw the doorway and arch to a scale of $1/20$ th full size using the approximate arc method.

Parabola

1. The principal cross-section of a sheet metal heat reflector is parabolic. The width of the open end of the reflector is 175 mm and its depth measured along its principal axis is 80 mm. Draw the curve representing the shape of the section of the heat reflector.

2. A piece of wire is bent into the form of a parabola. It fits into a rectangle which has a base length of 125 mm and a height of 100 mm. The open ends of the wire are 125 mm apart. By means of a single line show the shape of the wire.

3. A section on the centre line of a car headlamp reflector is a parabola, the focus of which is 20 mm from the back of the reflector, measured along the principal axis. The depth of the reflector along the axis is 180 mm. Construct the parabola.

4. The focus of a parabola is 50 mm from the directrix. Construct the curve with an axis 75 mm long. Construct the tangent and normal to the parabola at a point 60 mm from the directrix.

5. A point moves in a plane in such a way that its distance from a fixed point, called the focus, is equal to its shortest distance from a fixed straight line, called the directrix. Plot the locus of the moving point when the focus is 50 mm from the directrix. The maximum distance of the moving point is 150 mm from the focus.

6. An arch has a span of 50 metres and a central rise of 15 metres. The arch formed a parabolic curve either side of its centre line. Draw the arch to a scale of 10 mm = 20 mm.

7. Inscribe a parabola in a rectangle 120 mm by 80 mm.

8. Draw a straight line AB 125 mm long, and from C, the centre of AB, draw CD 100 mm long at right-angles to AB. A fixed point F is the mid-point of CD. A point P moves so that its distance from F is always equal to its distance from the line AB. Draw the locus of P to a maximum distance of 200 mm from AB. Draw a tangent to the curve at a point which is 100 mm from AB.

9. Draw a parabola given that its focus is 30 mm from the directrix. Draw the parabola by two different methods either side of the axis of symmetry.

Hyperbola

1. Construct the locus of a point P which moves so that its distance from a given point F and a given straight line AB are in the constant ratio of 3:2. The minimum and maximum distances of P from AB are 25 mm and 100 mm respectively.

2. Draw two straight lines AB and BC at right-angles to one another. These lines are the axes of a rectangular hyperbola. A point P on the curve is 25 mm above BC and 75 mm from AB. Draw the curve.

3. A hyperbola has its vertex 15 mm from the directrix and its focus 20 mm from the vertex. Draw the curve.

4. Construct a hyperbola with a distance of 25 mm between focus and directrix and an eccentricity of 8:3.

5. Draw the rectangular hyperbola of a cone of 80 mm dia. base and 100 mm altitude, the cut being 30 mm from the centre of the base.

6. Draw a straight line AB 125 mm long, and from C, the centre of AB, draw CD 175 mm long at right-angles to AB. A fixed point F on CD is 45 mm from C. A point P moves so that its distance from F is always 3/4 of its distance from the line AB. Draw the locus of P as it moves from a distance of 25 mm from AB to 175 mm from AB.

7. Construct a rectangular hyperbola having a point on the curve 15 mm from the vertical asymptote and 60 mm from the horizontal asymptote.

8. Construct a hyperbola given that the vertex is 25 mm from the directrix and that the unit of eccentricity is 3/1. Draw the tangent to a point P on the curve that is 100 mm from the focal point.

9. A cone, vertical height 120 mm and base 90 mm diameter is cut by a plane parallel to its axis and 15 mm from it. Draw the true shape of the section.

10. Draw the conic which has an eccentricity of 4/3 and a focus which is 40 mm from the directrix.

Cycloids

1. A wheel of 60 mm diameter rolls, without slipping, along a straight path. Plot the locus of a point P on the rim of the wheel and initially in contact with the path. Plot for one complete revolution.

2. A circular disc of 65 mm diameter rolls, without slipping, along a straight horizontal line. Plot the locus of a point on the periphery of the disc for 3/4 revolution of the disc. Construct the normal and tangent to the curve at the point where the disc comes to rest.

3. Draw an epicycloid and hypocycloid for a 50 mm rolling circle and a 150 mm diameter base circle.

4. A wheel of 30 mm diameter rolls, without slipping, around the inside of a cylinder whose inside diameter is 200 mm. Plot the locus of a point P situated on the periphery of the 30 mm wheel for one revolution of the wheel.

5. Plot the locus of a point A, 35 mm from the centre of a 100 mm diameter wheel, as the wheel rolls down a surface which slopes at 45° to the horizontal. Plot the locus for one complete revolution of the wheel.

6. A wheel of 40 mm diameter rolls, without slipping, along a horizontal flat path. Plot the locus of a point A on its circumference for one revolution of the wheel along the path. Plot also the locus of a point B which is situated at a distance of 25 mm from the wheel centre.

7. Two circles A and B, both of diameter 60 mm, represent the two wheels of a bicycle. The centres of A and B are 100 mm apart. C is the mid-point of the line AB. From C drop a perpendicular $CD = 20$ mm. The point D represents the pedal of the bicycle. Plot the locus of D as the crank CD makes two complete revolutions.

8. Circle A has a diameter of 40 mm. Circle B has a diameter of 60 mm and circle C has a diameter of 200 mm. Circle A rolls around the outside of circle C while circle B rolls around the inside of circle C. Circles A and B start from the same point P on the rim of circle C. Plot the locus of P on each circle as they move in a clockwise direction for one revolution each.

Helix

1. Construct a helix of 75 mm diameter and 50 mm pitch. Show one complete turn of the helix.

2. A helical spring is made of 12 mm square section material. The coils are 50 mm pitch and 10 mm outside diameter. Draw a longitudinal elevation showing 1½ turns of the spring.

3. Draw the plan and elevation of a helix with a lead of 50 mm which is described on the surface of a right circular prism whose diameter is 75 mm.

4. Two helices of lead equal to 60 mm are in the same plane and start on the same end of their base cylinders. One cylinder is of 55 mm diameter and the other of 45 mm diameter. Draw the helices for two revolutions.

5. A piece of thread is wrapped around a cylinder 140 mm long and of 100 mm diameter. Construct the helix formed by the thread travelling around the cylinder in three equal revolutions.

6. A cylinder 150 mm long, made from transparent material, has an outside diameter of 90 mm and an inside diameter of 55 mm. Two helical lines marked on its curved surface, one on the outside and one on the inside, have a common pitch of 65 mm. Draw the elevation of the cylinder showing both helices starting from the same point and completing two turns.

7. A point moves along and around the surface of a cylinder 60 mm in diameter, at a uniform rate, making one complete revolution in an axial length of 30 mm. Draw an elevation of the cylinder to show the locus of the point during two complete revolutions. Determine by construction the linear distance covered by the point when it has covered an axial length of 50 mm.

8. A helical spring, 65 mm outside diameter, is made of square section wire of 10 mm side. The axial length of the spring is 200 mm and there are 8 complete turns of the wire. Draw an elevation of a portion of the spring showing four complete turns.

9. A piece of tape 6 mm wide is wound around a tube 60 mm diameter and 200 mm long. The tape starts and finishes on a generator and occupies the whole length of the tube. Draw an elevation.

Involute/Archimedean spiral

1. Construct the involute to a base circle of diameter 35 mm and then draw a tangent to the locus at a point which is 100 mm from the centre of the circle. Construction for the involute and tangent are to be clearly shown.

2. Draw two convolutions of an Archimedean spiral such that in two revolutions the radius increases from 20 mm to 75 mm.

3. *A*, *B* and *C* are three points in that order on a straight line such that $AB = 40$ mm and $BC = 25$ mm. *B* is the pole of an Archimedean spiral. *C* is the nearest point on the curve and *A* another point on the first convolution of the curve. Draw the Archimedean spiral for two convolutions.

4. A cylinder is 50 mm in diameter and a piece of thin wire is equal in length to the circumference. One end of the wire is attached to *A*, a point on the curve of the cylinder. Draw the path of the free end of the wire when it is wound round the cylinder in a plane perpendicular to the axis of the cylinder. From a point 60 mm chord length from the free end of the wire construct a tangent to the circle representing the cylinder.

5. A taut chord is unwound from the circumference of a disc 100 mm in diameter. Plot the locus of a point on the chord and continue the curve until it reaches a position 100 mm from the centre of the disc.

6. A piece of string is wound tightly around a hexagon bar, each side of which is 25 mm long.
Plot the path traced out by the end of the string when it is unwound for one turn.

7. A gramophone disc is 175 mm in diameter. Plot the locus of the stylus as its travels from the outside edge to its stop position 25 mm from the centre. Assume the distance is covered in four revolutions.

8. A piece of wire *AB* is wrapped around a cylinder 50 mm in diameter in a clockwise direction. The length of wire is equal to the circumference of the cylinder.
Plot the path of the end *B* of the wire as it is wrapped around the cylinder.

Lines and lamina

1. A lies in the H.P. and is 30 mm from the V.P. B is 70 mm from the V.P. and is 55 mm from the H.P. The true length of the line AB is 85 mm. Draw the plan and elevation of the line.

2. A lies in the V.P. and is 10 mm from the H.P. The line AB is of length 80 mm. The elevation of AB is of length 60 mm and the projected length of AB on XY is 45 mm. Draw the plan and elevation of AB.

3. A line AB is of length 85 mm. A is 10 mm from the H.P. and 15 mm from the V.P. B is 55 mm from the H.P. and 45 mm from the V.P. The line does not cut the planes of reference. Draw the plan and elevation of the line.

4. In the triangle ABC, $AB = 60$ mm and $BC = CA = 75$ mm. AB lies in the H.P. parallel to and distance 45 mm from the V.P. C lies in the V.P. Draw the plan and elevation of the triangle.

5. A line AB is 100 mm long. End A is 35 mm above the H.P. and 50 mm in front of the V.P. End B is 5 mm above the H.P. and 10 mm in front of the V.P. Find the plan and determine its traces.

6. Construct a triangle ABC with AB 100 mm long, AC 125 mm long and BC 75 mm long. Bisect two of the angles to meet at O. ABC represents the plan of the ends of three guy ropes which are all in the same horizontal plane. O is the plan of a perpendicular pole which in elevation is 75 mm high. Draw the plan and elevation when the ropes are attached from the top of the pole to A, B and C. Find the total length in metres of rope required if $1 \text{ cm} = 1 \text{ m}$.
Note It does not matter about the triangular position of ABC in the plan as it will not affect the result.

7. A line AB is inclined at an angle of 30° to the H.P. and the plan of the line measures 125 mm. End A is 20 mm above the H.P. and 50 mm from the V.P. End B is 10 mm from the V.P. and is further than end A from the H.P. Draw the plan and elevation.

8. A line AB is of length 75 mm and its plan is of length 55 mm. The elevation of the line is inclined at 45° to XY. Draw the plan and elevation of the line.

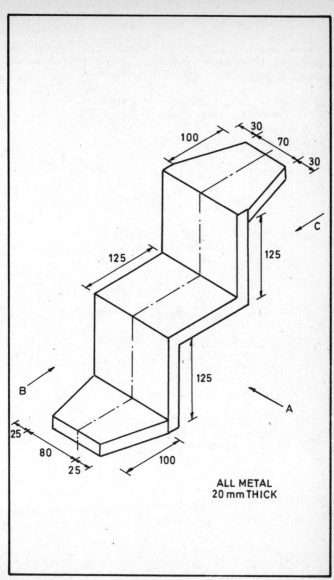

Figure 75

161

Orthographic projection

1. Draw, one-third full size, the following four views of the metal block shown in the isometric projection in Fig. 75 on the previous page. Use first-angle projection.

(a) A front elevation, in the direction of arrow *A*
(b) A side elevation, in the direction of arrow *B*
(c) A side elevation, in the direction of arrow *C*
(d) A plan projected from view (a)

Points to note specifically:
 (i) Spacing
 (ii) Scale
(iii) Correct use of types of line
(iv) Show all hidden details
 (v) Dimensions – at least three major sizes
(vi) Print name, the title, DRAWING BRACKET, scale, projection symbols and date

2. A Vee-block, used in engineering workshops, is shown opposite in Fig. 76.
Draw, full size, in third-angle projection the following views:

(a) A front elevation from *A*
(b) An end elevation from *B*
(c) A plan projected from view (a)

Add the following details
 (i) All hidden details
 (ii) Five leading dimensions
(iii) The title block with the words VEE-BLOCK

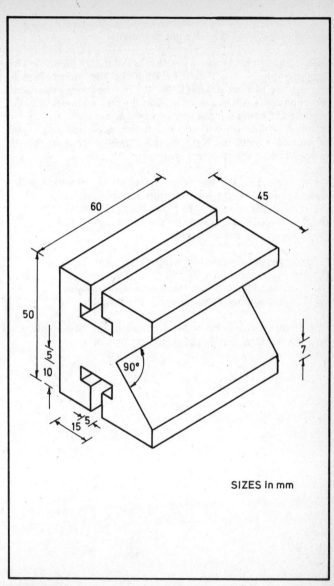

Figure 76

163

3. Figure 77 shows the components of a prefabricated swivel pulley. (The swivel items are not included.)

Two bushes (item 1) are inserted into the pulley (item 2). This sub-assembly is then bolted between the two plates (item 3) through the 10 mm diameter holes, the bushes acting as a spacer. The bolting is by means of a plain 10 mm diameter spindle, threaded M 10 at each end to take washers and nuts.
The swivel block (item 4) is bolted between the plates by means of four M 5 bolts and washers, the details of the four threads in item 4 being shown in one position.

Draw, scale 1:1, the following views of the assembled pulley showing suitable bolts, washers, nuts and spindle.
(a) A front elevation with the plates (item 3) vertical
(b) A sectional end elevation on the parallel plane E-E
Do not represent hidden detail.

Add to your drawing the following dimensions:
(a) The diameter of the pulley boss
(b) The assembled inside distance between the plates
(c) The radius of the cable groove in the pulley

Complete your drawing with your name, the title, scale and projection system used in the standard title block.

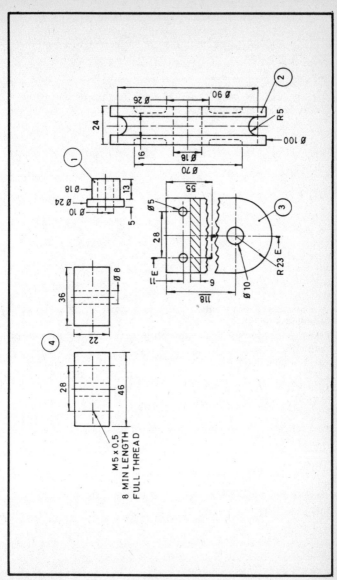

Figure 77

165

Auxiliary projection

1. Two views are given, in first-angle projection, of a bent metal bracket, Fig. 78a.
Draw full size:
(a) The given views
(b) An auxiliary **plan** at 45° in the direction of the arrow A to the new ground line X^1Y^1.

2. The plan and elevation of a hexagonal distance piece is shown in Fig. 78b.
Draw these views full size and project an auxiliary **elevation** on X^1Y^1.
Omit hidden details.

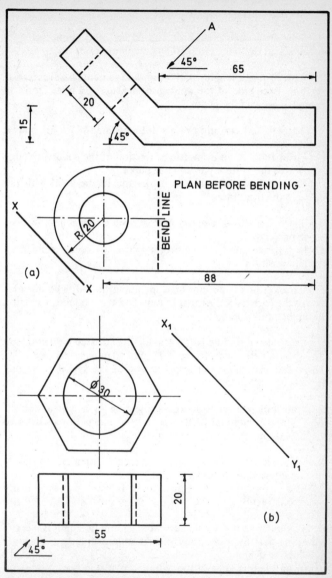

A

45°

65

20

15

45°

PLAN BEFORE BENDING

X

X

R 20

BEND LINE

(a)

88

X₁

Ø 30

Y₁

20

55

45°

(b)

Figure 78

Isometric/oblique projection

1. Draw an isometric cube of side 50 mm and upon each face construct an isometric circle of 50 mm diameter.

2. A prism has a length of 100 mm and is pentagonal in cross-section. Each side of the pentagon measures 25 mm. Draw an isometric view of the prism.

3. The plan and elevation of a solid machined block are shown in Fig. 79a.
(a) Draw full size an isometric projection of the solid with edge A towards the bottom part of your paper.
(b) Draw full size an oblique projection of the solid with the circle in the front face.

4. Figure 79b shows a hub-puller of uniform thickness in first-angle projection.
Draw full size an isometric projection of the component in an upright position.

5. A trinket box is 50 mm high including the lid. The distance across the corners of the top is 75 mm. Draw an oblique projection of the box full size.

6. A step-down spindle is 150 mm long. Each step is 50 mm long and the diameter of each step is 25 mm, 40 mm and 65 mm.
Draw full size an isometric projection of the spindle, showing it to its best advantage.

7. Draw full size an isometric projection of a Nut and Bolt. The bolt is a nominal M20 size and the nut is threaded on to its full extent.

8. A piece of tube 75 mm long has an external diameter of 60 mm and an internal diameter of 40 mm.
Make an isometric drawing of the tube full size, showing clearly your construction.

9. A cylinder 60 mm in diameter and 75 mm in length is pierced along its axis by a centrally placed square hole, the diagonal of which is 35 mm.
Draw an oblique view of the cylinder as it stands with one end on the H.P.

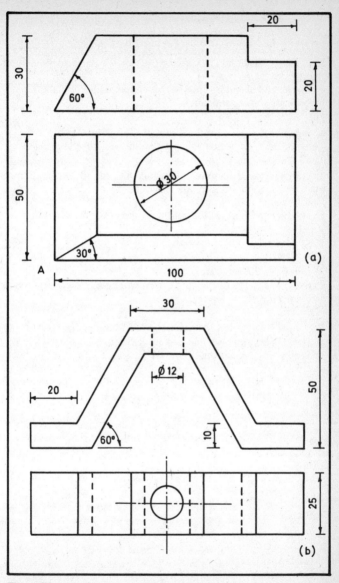

Figure 79

169

Sections/true shapes

1. Figure 80a shows the elevation and plan of a square pyramid. It is cut by a plane *XY* inclined at 45° to the horizontal and parallel to the vertical.
Draw the end elevation and the true shape of the cut plane. Cross-hatch your answer and label.

2. Figure 80b shows a cylinder cut by a horizontal plane *XY*.
Draw the elevation and project a plan showing the plane exposed.

3. A right cone of diameter 80 mm and altitude 100 mm is cut by a plane *XY*. The cutting plane is parallel to and distance 10 mm from the axis of the cone.
Draw the true shape of the cut plane and name the section.

4. A right cone of diameter 60 mm and 75 mm in height is cut by a plane *XY* that is parallel to an outside generator. The plane is 25 mm from the generator.
Draw a true shape of the cut surface and label the cross-hatched section correctly.

5. A hexagonal pyramid has a height of 75 mm and a base of side 20 mm. It is drawn so that a side of the base is parallel to the vertical plane. A cutting plane *XY* is drawn so that it intersects the axis of the pyramid at a point 50 mm from the base and at an angle of 45° to the horizontal.
Draw the true shape of the section.

6. A cylinder of length 200 mm has an inner diameter of 35 mm and walls that have a thickness of 10 mm. The cylinder is cut by a perpendicular plane *XY*, parallel to its axis and co-incidental with it.
Draw the cylinder and show the true shape of the sectioned cut *XY*.

7. Figure 80c shows two views of a shaped block.
Draw the views and add a sectioned end elevation.

8. A right cone has a base diameter of 100 mm and a height of 95 mm. It is cut by a plane at 45° to the horizontal and its base angle. Draw the true shape of the surface of the cut together with the auxiliary plan of the lower portion of the cone.

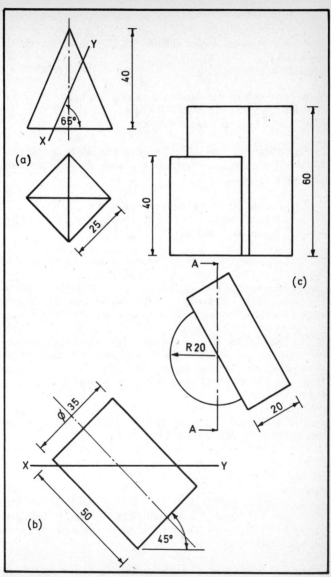

Figure 80

Developments

1. A right cone has a base diameter of 80 mm and an altitude of 75 mm.
Develop the surface of the cone by radial line development.

2. A right cone of base diameter 65 mm and height 80 mm is truncated by a line 30 mm from the base.
Develop the lower portion of the cone.

3. Figure 81a shows the side elevation of a metal-sheet drain.
Draw full size the development of the drain, the seam being on the shortest side.

4. A tray made of tinned plate is illustrated in Fig. 81b.
Draw the development of the tin in such a way that the number of joints is kept to a minimum.

5. A small scoop is to be made to the dimensions given in Fig. 81c.
Draw the development of the shape of the metal required for the body of the scoop to have the joint at *AB*. Ignore the thickness of the metal and do not allow for any overlap.

6. Figure 81d shows three pipes, each of 50 mm diameter and of no consequential thickness. The axis of each cylinder is in the same plane and ultimately form a bend of 90°.
Draw the given view and develop the pipe *A* with *XY* as the joint line.

7. The development of the sides of a prism is cut by an inclined plane as shown in Fig. 81e.
The base of the prism is a regular hexagon. Draw two elevations and a plan of the fabricated prism and obtain the true shape of the surface cut by the inclined plane.

8. The shape of the development *ABCD* is shown in Fig. 81f.
The shape is to be made into a parallel sided cylinder with *DC* on the horizontal plane. Draw an elevation which clearly shows the join of *AD* to *BC*.

9. Develop the surface of a pentagonal trinket box of side 25 mm and height 30 mm.

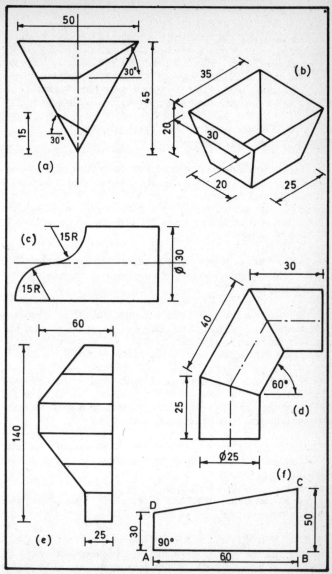

Figure 81

173

Intersections

1. Two cylinders, one 60 mm in diameter and the other 30 mm in diameter, are arranged so that the smaller cylinder passes through the larger. When the larger cylinder is vertical the smaller pipe makes an angle of 45° to the horizontal. In the plan the centre lines of the two cylinders are 10 mm apart. Draw an elevation and plan to show clearly the curve of intersection.

2. Two cylindrical pipes intersect as shown in Fig. 82a.
Draw the plan and elevation of the interpenetration.

3. A sphere of diameter 80 mm is intersected by a vertical cylinder of 65 mm diameter. In the plan the centre line of the cylinder passes through a point 6 mm from the centre of the sphere and on a line drawn at 30° through the centre of the sphere. Draw the plan and elevation of the two solids showing clearly the line of intersection.

4. In Fig. 82b a cone and cylinder intersect. Draw the two views given and complete the line of interpenetration showing your construction clearly.

5. A hexagonal prism 100 mm in length and of side 25 mm is intersected by a cylinder 75 mm long and 35 mm in diameter. The axes of the prism and cylinder coincide in the same plane but at 60° to the horizontal. Draw the line of intersection.

6. A square tube is placed directly above and on top of a right circular cone. The axes of the cone and tube coincide. If the faces of the tube are parallel to the vertical planes draw the curve of intersection between tube and cone.

7. The height of a right circular cone is 90 mm and the base diameter is 100 mm. The cone is pierced by a square hole of side 35 mm. The axis of the hole intersects the axis of the cone 35 mm above the base and is parallel to the base.
Draw an elevation of the cone looking in a direction at right-angles to the vertical faces of the hole.

8. Two pipes of 75 mm and 50 mm diameter meet at right-angles and are joined in such a way that the combined pipes can be placed flat against a wall. Draw a plan and elevation of the pipes showing the line of intersection.

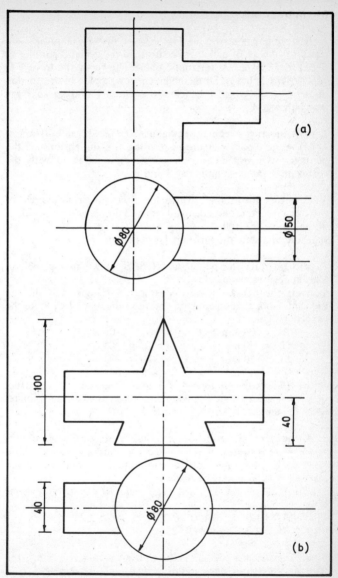

Figure 82

175

Miscellaneous questions

1. Two spheres, shown in Fig. 83a in first-angle projection, stand on the H.P. and their centres lie on a plane parallel to the vertical plane. A horizontal plane, shown by the trace VT, cuts the two spheres. Draw the given view, a plan of the portion of the spheres which are below the line VT and an auxiliary plan below X_1Y_1.

2. (a) Construct a regular pentagon $ABCDE$ with side 70 mm.

(b) As a separate figure, but using the dimensions of the pentagon constructed in (a), construct a parabola with the vertex at D and terminating at A and B.

3. Construct the triangle which has a circumscribing circle of 116 mm diameter, one side of 80 mm and the remaining two sides in the ratio of 57:100.
Measure and state the three angles of the triangle.

4. (a) Construct the pentagon $HGFCB$ shown in Fig. 83b to the dimensions given below.
Convert the pentagon into an isosceles triangle ABC having the same area as the pentagon and the same base BC. State the vertical height.

$BC = 100$ mm	$<C = 90°$
$HB = 80$ mm	$<B = 120°$
$FC = 80$ mm	$<H = 30°$
	$<F = 60°$

(b) Redraw the triangle ABC and, on the side BC, construct in it a trapezium $DECB$ having an area ¾ that of the triangle. State the length of DE.

5. A photographic reduction of a map is made. On the photograph 4 km is represented by a line 127 mm long. Construct an open divided diagonal scale to read up to 5 km and from which distances of 100 m may be read.
Use the scale to draw a plan of an airfield $ABCD$ with dimensions in km as follows:

$AB = 1.8$	$CD = 2.2$	$AC = 3.2$
$BC = 2.7$	$AD = 2.4$	

6. (a) Construct a triangle ABC with an area $= 3200$ mm², the base $AB = 110$ mm long and the vertical angle $ACB = 80°$.

(b) Use a graphical construction to determine $\sqrt{5}$.

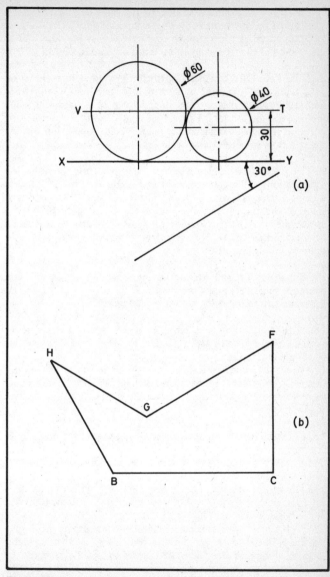

Figure 83

7. The piece of tinplate shown in Fig. 84a is formed into a cylinder of 48 mm diameter with AB meeting A^1B^1. Draw a plan and elevation of the cylinder so formed with the join AB in the middle of the front elevation. Show any hidden detail.

8. A design study consists of wire rods welded into the form of a truncated pyramid as shown in Fig. 84b. On the front face a further rod is welded in the form of a parabola when seen in the given plan. The vertex is at C and the terminating points at A and B. Construct the plan and elevation given, adding the parabola in both views. Scale 1:1.

9. Two different triangles ABC can be drawn from the following information: $AB = 120$, $BC = 70$ and angle $BAC = 30°$. On the common base AB and with the apexes C and C^1 on opposite sides of the base, draw the two different triangles to form a quadrilateral $ACBC^1$. Construct a similar quadrilateral with an area twice that of $ACBC^1$. Construct a square equal in area to the new quadrilateral.

10. Construct a parallelogram having diagonals of 120 mm and 80 mm respectively and a perimeter of 270 mm.
State the size of the sides of the parallelogram.

11. With centres on the corners of an isosceles triangle of vertical height 80 mm and base 63 mm, three circles are drawn of 40 mm diameter.
Construct the centre and draw a fourth circle so that it contains the two circles on the base and touches externally the circle on the vertex of the triangle. State the diameter to the nearest millimetre.

12. Construct an open divided diagonal scale, scaled 1:5, to read up to 1 metre in units of 10 mm.
Show, by a firm line drawn on the scale, a reading of 0.77 m.

13. The beater of a vacuum carpet sweeper is made of a cylinder of wood with a strip of rubber set on edge in a helical groove cut in the cylinder.
The wooden cylinder is ⌀50 mm and the rubber strip has negligible thickness but is to be opaque and projecting from the cylinder 15 mm. Draw in elevation two turns of the helix made by the outer edge of the rubber strip. The pitch of the helix is 70 mm. Show any hidden detail.

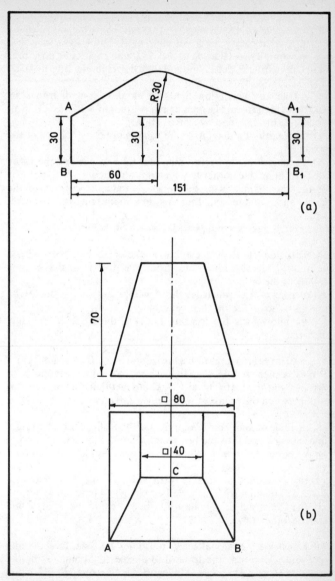

Figure 84

14. Crank AB, shown in Fig. 85a, is hinged at A and oscillates 45° each side of the vertical centre line. B is hinged to allow CD to pass through the pivot slide at P. Draw the locus of C for one complete oscillation of AB. If D must approach no nearer than 10 mm from P, determine and state the minimum length of CD.

15. A frame on which floodlights are mounted is made from scaffold tubes in the form of a rectangular prism, 4 m × 2.75 m × 1.75 m. To a scale of 1:50, find by construction:
(a) the length of a diagonal tube joining opposite corners of the frame;
(b) the angles made by the diagonal tube to each of the three tubes forming one corner to which it is attached.
Ignore the diameters of the tubes. Notate the corners of the frame and tabulate your four answers, identifying the measurements clearly.
Hint: First make a small pictorial sketch of the frame.

16. The side of a fume cabinet is shown in Fig. 85b, with a ventilating duct leading out from the top into the sloping ceiling of the lab.
To a scale of 1:5 construct the development of the duct. The joint is to be on the shortest generator.
Ignore allowances for jointing and the thickness of the duct material.

17. A point O is 55 mm from a horizontal line CD. A second point P moves such that $4PN = 5PO$ – where PN is the perpendicular distance of the point P from CD. Construct that part of the locus of P between the points at which $PN = 118$ mm.

18. A circle of diameter 30 mm rolls without slipping on a straight line inclined at 30° to the horizontal. Plot the locus of P, a point on the circumference of the circle, for one complete revolution.

19. (a) Construct a triangle with sides in the proportion of 1.5:2.5:3.0 and having an inscribed circle of 44 mm diameter.
    (b) Construct the smallest escribed circle to the triangle and state its diameter.

20. Construct a diagonal scale, ten times full size, to show mm and tenths of a mm and to read to a max. of 20 mm. Using the scale, construct a triangle ABC with AB 17.4 mm, BC 13.8 mm and AC 11 mm.

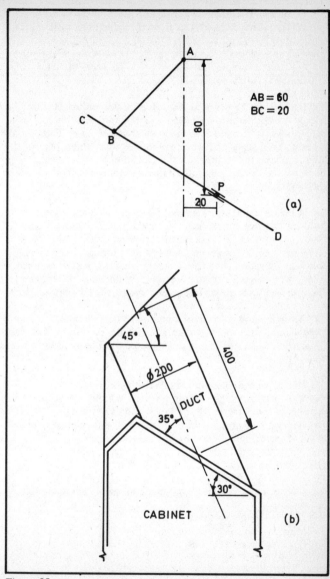

AB = 60
BC = 20

80

20

(a)

45°

Ø 200

DUCT

400

35°

30°

CABINET

(b)

Figure 85

181

21. In the mechanism shown in the half-way position in Fig. 86a, *OE* rotates about *O* from *A* to *B*. In the same time, both motions being uniform, *G* moves from *C* to *D*. *EF* and *FG* are two links pivoted at *E*, *F* and *G*. Construct the locus of the mid-point of *EF* for the complete movement of *OE*. *OE* = 70 mm; *EF* = 160 mm; *FG* = 100 mm. Scale 1:2.

22. Figure 86b shows a sector of a circle, radius 90 mm, on which an equilateral triangle, side 60 mm, has been drawn. The sector is formed into a cone giving a base diameter of 70 mm. To a scale of 1:1 drawn an elevation and a plan of the cone showing the triangle on the elevation only. The seam is to be positioned as the generator nearest to the vertical plane. Show hidden detail.

23. A cylinder 100 mm long and 500 mm diameter is set up on a lathe to revolve on its axis. A sharp pencil is moved with its point in contact with the cylinder along the tool rest at a constant velocity of 45 mm for one revolution of the cylinder. Draw an elevation of the cylinder showing the pencil line formed over the full length of the cylinder. A not-to-scale drawing of the lathe set up is shown in Fig. 86c. Name the curve produced.

24. A torch, showing a circular beam of 80 mm diameter, is shone onto a wall, the beam making an angle of 45° to the wall. Construct, scale 1:1, the true shape of the illumination on the wall.

25. Construct the following regular polygons:
(a) The largest octagon within a square 60 mm side so that four corners of the octagon fall on the diagonals of the square.
(b) An octagon fitting within a square 60 mm side so that four sides of the octagon fall on the four sides of the square.
(c) An octagon with the shortest diagonals 30 mm.
(d) A pentagon with the diagonals 45 mm.

26. Construct a clockwise Archimedean spiral having the following properties:
(a) shortest radius vector: 25 mm
(b) longest radius vector: 90 mm
(c) number of convolutions: 1.75
Scale 1:1.

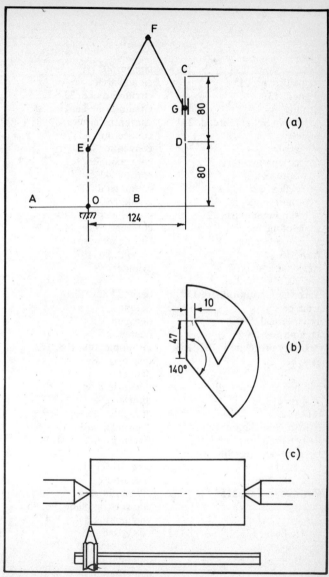

Figure 86

Index

Examination hints

1. General advice

No student should enter for an examination for which he/she has made little attempt at preparation. Preparation or study is the key-note to success. Lack of study generally means disappointment and the students will not only have let themselves down, but also those teachers who have worked so hard on their behalf.

Real study means long hours of hard work and sacrifice at a time when it is particularly tempting to be engaged in other activities of a much more exciting nature.

In technical drawing, study should be an active participation and not one of trying to sit down and learn by reading a book. It is very much a practical subject and, as with any such subject, practice, practice and yet more practice will pay dividends. As soon as the student starts the course, he or she should put in as many hours as possible every week. It is not the type of subject that can be crammed into the last few weeks before the actual examination. It soon becomes evident to me which of my students is keeping up with homework and diligently practising any geometric topics we may have discussed. Failure to do so only serves to accelerate the ever widening gap between them and the less diligent student.

Most technical drawing examinations at CSE and GCE consist of two papers: an engineering drawing paper and a geometrical drawing paper. One hopes that the student will know the format that his/her particular examination follows and that they will have had ample opportunity to have seen and practised upon past papers. My own students 'sit' a past paper every week from Easter onwards. Not only does this give valuable practice in the technical sense but also means that the 'real' examination holds less of a fear for them.

Examinations are no longer a question of learning material, to be recalled ad verbatim, parrot fashion. Questions are now designed to test the students' **understanding** and their ability to **solve problems.** So although the material in this book is rather clearly defined into specific topics, the examination questions will tend to set problems that will test the ability to use perhaps several combined topics in the answer.

Whatever the examination, the most important single factor is to **read** the questions and then read them again. All too often students only read what they think they see, which is generally what they want to see, but not necessarily what is actually written. Make absolutely sure that the question is fully understood.

Do not be tempted to rush straight into an answer. Read **all** the questions several times through before making a mark against those likely to be the ones!

2. Paper I
The first paper in technical drawing is the engineering drawing section, in which a component in orthographic projection will have to be re-arranged or completed or 'looked at' from another view-point. Most examining boards now allow some ten minutes before the examination starts for the reading of the paper when the students are not permitted to do any formal drawing. It is a chance really to read the paper and assess what is required. To my mind, it is also an opportunity to sketch on a rough piece of paper a pictorial view of the component. It does not matter how poor the sketch is, as long as it gives some clearer idea of what the object looks like. Surely it must be easier to attempt the answer with a small pictorial drawing to which one can refer from time to time.

Some boards include a second question in this section and it generally takes the form of a quick isometric/oblique drawing or freehand sketch of some component or tool. It may be stated on the front cover of the examination paper how many marks this second question is worth. It is important not to spend too much time on it as no matter how well you answer the question there will be a maximum mark allowance for it, perhaps something in the order of ten per cent.

Having read the paper, the student can start in earnest. **It is essential to make a start** and not to sit looking at the paper telling oneself how impossible it is! Work out the overall sizes, length, width, height and at least start to position the work in terms of layout. Remember it is not important to work out the positioning to the nearest millimetre! Position the centre lines and draw these in in top line density. Build up the framework around these centre lines but do not be too concerned at this stage with the detail. Try to position any circles or arcs lightly. Remember that it is easier to draw straight lines to circles rather than the other way round. But above all concentrate on the main **body** of the component. Nuts and bolts, handles, spindles, etc., are all best left until much later.

The examiner can only mark what is before him – he cannot visualise what one might have done! Therefore rather than spend all one's time on **one view,** project the work around **all three views** at the same time. A detail or line in the front elevation should immediately be transferred around to the other two views. There are only so many marks per view, no matter how expertly one may have drawn it. Better to pick up marks on all **three** views. The main bulk of the three views should be completed **before** one starts to think of the 'extras' like nuts and bolts, etc.

Printing and dimensioning are examples where valuable extra marks can be obtained. A relatively good percentage of the overall marks for the paper is awarded to the area of printing, presentation, quality and dimensioning. Regular practice of printing pays dividends and when dimensioning is poorly done it spoils the overall look and is sheer laziness. These marks can be the difference between success and failure.

Finally, the examiner is looking for **draughtsmanship** as well as a correct solution. Present your work neatly and clearly. First impressions are very important and a hard-working, tired examiner welcomes a piece of work that has a little style and craftsmanship.

3. Paper II
The second paper in technical drawing is concerned with plane and solid geometry. Students will generally be given a choice of questions in this paper, perhaps in the order of five questions from seven.

The most important aspect of this particular paper is **time.** Each question will have a **set** mark allocation and it is therefore pointless spending all the time answering perhaps only two questions in superb fashion. It is much more valid to work out exactly how much time one can afford to spend on **each** question. In a two hour paper with five questions the time would be twenty-four minutes per question. Make a time scale on a scrap piece of paper and keep a careful eye on the time. In this way one will at least be giving oneself a fair chance.

Make sure that the question is fully understood. Are the examiners looking for a stated answer in terms of measurement? If so do not forget to give one. The student should be very clear in his/her mind exactly what area or topic the question is based upon. Is it a loci, and if it is, what kind? Have they asked the student to draw or construct?

Most questions will ask the student to repeat or copy some aspect that is already included in the question: e.g., **'Draw the given views** and then construct an auxiliary to the new ground line X_1Y_1'. There are marks allocated for simply drawing the given views, so at least it is possible to pick up some marks even if the next step required is beyond the student.

Make the constructions perfectly clear and do not erase any important lines. The examiner wants to know how one has arrived at the solution. Keep the work neat and in an orderly fashion. It is most aggravating for the examiner to have to search for any answer. He is working under pressure and is more likely to be generous to papers that he can mark in a straight-forward way.

The topics covered in this book, as previously stated, are very self-contained. It is unlikely that **all** the questions on the paper will appear in the same self-contained manner. Some questions are likely to be 'wrapped-up' in such a way as to appear unrelated to most of the work that has been covered. A typical example:

> 'The figure shows the plan of a factory entrance and a run line fixed at *A* and *B*. The line is 34 m long and is used to limit the run of a guard dog. The dog is fixed to the line by a ring and a chain on his collar. The ring and chain allow the dog to reach out 3 m further than the stretched running line.
> Draw the plan of the yard, scale 1:200 and by construction show the extent of the area that the dog can cover.'

The question is about a loci and requires the plotting of a point (the dog) along a fixed but flexible line (the run). It could have been re-worded as such:

> 'Two points A and B, x distance apart are joined by a longer flexible line of length 34 m. A point P moves from A to B at the same time keeping the line taut. A further point X is attached rigidly to P. Plot the locus of X as P moves from A to B.'
> (The question is made a little more problematic by asking the student to use a scale.)

However, there will be questions that the student will instantly recognise as belonging to a particular topic area. Choose carefully. There are topic areas that, even if one knows the answer or one feels very confident about answering, require some time actually to put the work down on paper. For example, any loci problem, or auxiliary, development, intersection question will, because of the very nature of the work involved, take time. They need to be drawn carefully and accurately, but above all they have to be **plotted.** It is this plotting that takes time. Some questions like lines in space, tangency or equal area problems do not require the same time, because they are demanding of the student's basic geometrical knowledge. If one is unable to visualise lines in space, no amount of plotting will give the answer. There are then really two areas of questions, those that can be answered by sheer graft and an understanding of **solid** geometry and those involving **plane** geometry that require a knowledge of geometrical proofs.

Whatever the question, the answer should be clearly labelled. All too often students omit any number and letter reference to their work. Loci should be numbered/lettered A_1, A_2, A_3, etc., and any work plotted should be clearly defined. If the examiner has to assess where any student went wrong, it is so much easier for him to do so if he can follow the order of progression as it was plotted. Do not be timid in your approach to this numbering/lettering; so many times one has virtually to use a magnifying glass to find the references. The numbering and lettering are an **indication** to the examiner that you have followed a logical and carefully sequenced route to your answer. This may not be so, but at least it will create a favourable impression!

4. In conclusion
The student will have to work hard for his/her success. There

is no easy way or short cut. Past examination papers give a very useful guide as to the type and range of questions to expect.

Hopefully this small book will be of some assistance in the answering of the questions. It is not by any means the only way and students should refer to as many different books and notes as they have available.

Finally, the best and most positive way to revise is to 'do' the work and then to assess its correctness or otherwise.

Good Luck.

key facts

Key Facts
Revision Section

Key Facts Revision Section

Chapter 1   Introduction to technical drawing

The main point to remember about this chapter is that a student cannot expect to develop his skill and talent without the proper equipment. This does not necessarily mean expensive or elaborate equipment. It does mean buying sensibly, a few rather good instruments in preference to a whole array of inaccurate ones. Do not be tempted by cheap offers or clever packaging. Seek the advice of experienced and professional draughtsmen and teachers.

Lines and lettering
Lines must be clear, even and 'crisp'. They should meet at the corners accurately and not fall short of any distance. All construction lines should be in 4H pencil and only just visible. The final top line should be in 2H and must be super-imposed directly over the construction line. There must be no 'ghosting' or 'double vision'.

Lettering should be clear and of a definite style. Remember that the drawing has to be 'read' by someone else and it is best, therefore, to avoid 'arty' lettering but rather confine oneself to the upright and more precise type.

Dimensioning
Make sure that you understand the British Standards and I.S.O. recommendations on this aspect of the work. **Unbroken lines** ending in **arrow-heads** go right up to the **lead** lines. Numerals are placed either **above** or to the **left** of the dimensioning lines. All measurements are in **millimetres** unless otherwise stated. Avoid placing any dimension actually **on** the drawing.

Chapter 2   Lines and angles

Questions set solely on lines and angles do not appear very often on any of the examining boards' papers. However, as every topic must include some line or angle or requires knowledge of line and angle proofs, then it is advisable to know as much of the basic work as is possible.

The **vertex** is the point where two **arms** meet and the resultant **angle** is measured in degrees.

A complete circle contains $360°$ and when divided up into four equal parts forms angles of $90°$ which are known as **right-angles.**

An **obtuse** angle is more than 90° but less than 180°. An **acute** angle is less than 90° and a **reflex** angle is more than 180° but less than 360°.

Complementary angles are two angles which add up to 90° and **supplementary** angles are two angles which add up to 180°.

Angles can be drawn with a **protractor** and/or **set-squares** but only **constructed** with compasses.

It is important to know how to construct an angle of 90° and an angle of 60° with the aid of compasses. From this knowledge and by learning how to bisect and trisect any angle, then angles of 45°, 30°, 20° are possible, followed by further division into 15°, 10°, 7½°, 5°, 3°, etc. By adding or subtracting any of these angles, it is possible to construct most angles.

The division of lines by **ratio** or **proportion** is also essential background knowledge and avoids direct mathematical calculation to solve a problem.

Chapter 3   Scales

In all the questions referring to scales the accent is on the use of diagonal scale rather than plain scale. Always follow the format of the diagrams as in Chapter 3, leaving the first unit for the breakdown into the smaller divisions and start the 0 thereafter.

Make sure that you state the scale at the bottom of your work, especially if you are answering an actual drawing question, like orthographic projection. It is advisable to state your scale in terms of 2:1, 1:2, 1:5, etc.

The very first point to establish is what your scale is **representing.** If, for example, you are asked to construct a scale of 40 mm to 1 metre, then for every 40 mm that you draw on your paper, 1 metre is represented on the real object. You next establish what total distance is needed on the real object. The question might state that you have to read up to 3 metres. If this is the case then on your paper you would draw a line 120 mm long (40 mm × 3 required metres). Each 40 mm on the paper is a unit, that only measures a representative metre. However, it may be necessary to measure smaller distances than 1 metre and if this is so, then the unit to the left of 0 is subdivided. The question may ask you to read down to units of 4 cm.

There are 100 cm in a metre, so the unit to the left of 0 must be sub-divided into 100. But we are asked for units of 4 cm and so the sub-division need only be into 25. The most convenient way of dividing this would be by 5 units along the base line and 5 units on the vertical line.

Remember that the vertical column on the diagonal scale can be any reasonable height as the measurement forward is not affected by the height.

Chapter 4   Triangles

Questions that deal solely with problems relating to triangles are very infrequent – but very many questions have some involvement with the triangle, being the most basic of all the plane figures and the student should be conversant with the many proofs.

An **equilateral** triangle has all three sides and angles equal, while a **scalene** triangle has all sides and angles unequal. An **isosceles** triangle has two sides and the angles opposite to these sides equal. The **hypotenuse** is the side opposite to an angle of $90°$ in a **right-angled** triangle. An **obtuse** triangle has one obtuse angle and an **acute** triangle has all three angles acute.

The three angles of any triangle add up to $180°$; the **vertex** is the point opposite to the base and the height is often referred to as the **altitude.**

Any triangle in a semi-circle, with the **diameter** as the base, has a right-angle at the circumference.

Any triangles with a **common base** within a circle will have the same angles at the circumference and the angle from that common base to the centre of the circle will be twice that at the circumference.

The right-angled triangle is useful in the working out of square roots. Using the **theorem of Pythagoras,** the square on the hypotenuse is equal to the sum of the squares on the other two sides.

The drawing of triangles themselves is a case of the student **learning** the basic constructions. The student will have to be given data like the length of sides, the angles, the altitude, the perimeter, the ratio of the sides, or indeed any combination of these facts in order to work out any particular problem. The only real way to learn this type of work is by constant practice of the basic geometry and this will pay dividends later.

Chapter 5   Quadrilaterals

There are many questions that involve knowledge of quadrilaterals. As with triangles, the problems do not deal specifically with them but rather use them as a base from which to solve **further** problems.

The most common form of quadrilateral, which means four sides, is the square. A square has all four sides and all four angles equal, the angles all being $90°$. The sum of the angles in any quadrilateral add up to $360°$.

A quadrilateral is sometimes known as a **quadrangle.**

A **rectangle** has opposite sides equal and all angles are $90°$. A **rhombus** has all sides equal but is not right-angled and a **rhomboid** has opposite sides equal but is not right-angled.

Trapezium–two sides parallel, **trapezoid**–no sides parallel and **trapezion or kite** has pairs of adjacent sides equal and is symmetrical about an axis or centre line with its diagonal at right-angles to that axis.

In all the four-sided figures that constitute quadrilaterals, the line joining one corner (vertex) to the opposite corner is called a **diagonal.**

Chapter 6   Polygons

Polygons generally refer to those figures which have more than four straight sides. The word means 'many-sided' and those polygons that have sides and angles equal are called **regular,** while those polygons that have unequal sides and angles are known as **irregular.**

Each regular polygon is given a specific name depending on the number of sides it contains. Thus, **pentagon**–five, **hexagon** –six, **heptagon**–seven, **octagon**–eight, **nonagon**–nine and **decagon**–ten-sided.

197

Regular polygons are termed **convex** because each of their internal angles is less than 180°. If the polygon has an internal angle of more than 180° it is known as **re-entrant.**

The **diagonal** of a polygon is the line from one corner to another except on **adjacent** corners.

A regular polygon may be constructed upon a given line or within a given circle and the student should learn these constructions as a great many orthographic elevations require this knowledge.

A most useful fact is that any polygon can be constructed by the use of **angles.** The angle **subtended** at the centre of any regular polygon is determined by the formula $360° \div N$ where N is the number of sides. Thus a pentagon has an angle of 72° subtended at its centre from one base side.

A **hexagon** is the easiest of all the regular polygons as each side is equal to the **radius** of the circle that circumscribes it.

Regular polygons can be drawn therefore with the aid of **protractors** and/or **set-squares** but the student must take note of the wording. For example, if the question says **'construct'**, then it means just that, and compasses and learned construction must be used. If the question says 'draw' then any means of arriving at the solution is considered correct.

Chapter 7   Circles and tangents

Questions involving circles and tangency occur frequently in examination papers because of the close association with mechanisms and loci.

The circle has more named parts to it than any other figure. The straight line drawn through the centre of a circle and touching the **circumference** at both ends is the **diameter.** An **arc** is any part of the circumference, which is the line that encloses the circle.

A **chord** is a straight line joining any two points on the circumference. A **sector** is that part of the circle formed by drawing two radii and the arc which they cut off. The circle is then divided into two sectors–**major** and **minor.** A **segment** is part of a circle bounded by a chord and an arc. This also divides the circle into a major and a minor segment.

The quadrant divides the circle into four equal sections while the **semi-circle** is exactly half a circle.

A **tangent** is a straight line which touches but does not cut the circle and the exact point of contact is called the **point of tangency.**
The **normal** is the radius from the centre of the circle to the point of tangency.
The **radius** is any straight line from the centre to the circumference and is generally the means by which the circle is drawn.

Concentric circles have the same centre but different radii while **eccentric** circles have different centres as well as different radii.

Circumscribed circles are those drawn round a figure yet touching its every point and **inscribed** circles are those drawn inside a figure touching all the boundary surfaces.

Mathematically, the circumference of a circle is nearly $3^{1}/_{7}$ times its diameter or 3.1416 and in formulae is shown by the Greek letter π (pi).

Chapter 8   Equal areas & similar figures

Equivalent areas and similar figures are extremely varied in their context and the student must know the basic proofs in this chapter.

The **area** of any figure is the amount of **space** enclosed by its boundary while a **similar** figure is one which has the **same shape** but not necessarily the same area.

The most frequently used proof is that which reduces a given figure to a triangle of equal area. This usually means a shape such as a quadrilateral reduced to a triangle. From this point the **triangle** can be reduced to a **rectangle** and the rectangle to a **square.** It is therefore possible to be asked to reduce a given figure of any number of sides to a square of equal area. In other words, the student could be asked to find by construction the **square area** of any figure.

It is also important to be able to **divide** or **proportion** an area of any figure. This is to say to divide the figure for example into one half or one fifth of its area. It may be required to proportion any figure in the ratio of say 3:5:7 of its area.

There are several different types of construction concerning similar figures. The main difference being between those constructions required to enlarge or reduce the **length of side,** and those constructions required to enlarge or reduce the figure in **ratio to area.**

Chapter 9   Loci mechanisms

In loci mechanisms always study the motivating parts, i.e., the part or parts that are to be the driving force of the mechanism. Having established which part is moving all the other parts (this is usually in the form of a rotating crank about a fixed point), plot this area first. In the case of crank tracing a circle, divide the circle into at least eight equal sections or plotting points around the circumference. **Mark** these points A_1, A_2, A_3, etc., clearly and boldly. From the point A_1 work out all the other linkage and mark each new plot B_1, B_2, C_1, C_2, etc. It is absolutely essential to plot **as you work** and not to draw masses of lines and then try to remember which point refers to what reference letter. The whole essence of loci mechanisms is that it is an exercise in logical and systematic plotting and recording.

Make sure that you fully understand all the differences between pivots, slides, fixed points and points that rotate or oscillate.

Some loci move in predictable ways, in that the conditions that govern their movement are fixed. These loci are given special names.

Ellipse
An ellipse is the locus of a point which moves so that the sum of its distance from two fixed points, known as the **focal points,** is a constant. The constant is the **major** axis of the ellipse.

A point that moves from one position to another in relation to some other point and following a definitive path, traces a line known as a locus (plural loci).

It is only possible to draw an ellipse when given the length of the major and minor axes or the major axis and the position of the focal points.

Construction of an ellipse can be by the **concentric circle method, trammel method, focal point method** or the **approximate arc method** although visually the neatest is not considered an exact construction.

The **tangent** to a point on an ellipse is constructed by joining both focal points to the point on the curve. Bisecting the resulting angle will give the normal. The tangent is the line at right-angles to this normal and the point on the curve.

Parabola
A parabola is the locus of a point whose distance from a fixed point, called the focus, and a straight line, called the directrix, is equal.

Individually, parabolas, hyperbolas, cycloids, involutes, helices and Archimedean spirals do not appear as frequently in examination papers as other topics. Taken as a whole it is fair to say that at least **one** of them will appear as frequently as the other separate topics.

There are two main constructions for the drawing of a parabolic curve. The first method is that in which the student is given the distance of the **focal point** from the **directrix.** Because it is a parabola the vertex is known immediately, being half way between the given focus and the directrix.

The second method is that in which information is given concerning the **rectangle** encasing the parabola. The point to remember here is that the rectangle should be divided in half by the **axis of symmetry** and each half plotted separately. If the length of the rectangle is divided into eight units then the **half-width** is also divided into eight units.

Parabolic reflectors are to be found in searchlights, spotlights, headlights, electric heating appliances, reflecting telescopes, radar and radio receivers.

Hyperbola
A hyperbola is the locus of a point whose distance from a fixed

point, the focus, to a straight line, the directrix, has a constant ratio greater than one.

A hyperbola is rather more complicated than the parabola in that the focus and the position of the vertex have to be given. The vertex will be in a stated ratio between the directrix and the focal point. This ratio is sometimes known as the **unit of eccentricity.**

When setting out to plot the hyperbola I would suggest that you make up a proportional scale in whatever ratio is given. For example, if the ratio is 3:2 draw a line *AB* 3 units long (it does not matter what length each unit is), draw another line *AC,* at an acute angle to *AB,* two units long. Join the end of *AB* to the end of *AC* giving *BC* which is the datum line. Any distance along *AB* can be 'read' on *AC* by drawing a line **parallel** to *BC.* In this way any distance will be in the ratio of 3:2.

The other construction for a hyperbola is based on being given the asymptotes and a point *P* on the hyperbolic curve.

Cycloid
A cycloid is the locus of a point on the circumference of a circle which rolls, without slipping, along a fixed straight line.

Most questions on cycloids include the phrase, 'without slipping', and it is simply a safeguard against any student making the point that most wheels under traction will 'slip' and lose energy in the initial movement forward. It has therefore to be included to be positive and not leave any cause for doubt.

As with all loci it is extremely important to plot carefully every move and to **record** it as you work on the question.

Inferior trochoid (or curtate trochoid)
The inferior trochoid is the locus of a point inside a circle which rolls, without slipping, along a fixed straight line.

Superior trochoid (or prolate trochoid)
The superior trochoid is the locus of a point outside a circle which rolls, without slipping, along a fixed straight line.

Epicycloid
An epicycloid is the locus of a point on the circumference of a circle which rolls, without slipping, around the outside of another fixed circle.

Hypocycloid
A hypocycloid is the locus of a point on the circumference of a circle when the circle rolls, without slipping, along the inside of another fixed circle.

In all the cases above, the point that is being traced is fixed rigidly to the rolling circle and when stepping out the circumference of the circle it is the circumference of the motivating circle that is used.

The circumference of any circle can be calculated mathematically but it is considered accurate enough to divide the circumference into at least eight divisions with the use of dividers. This distance can then be stepped off along the base line.

The profile of rack-teeth on cast gears is based on the cycloid.

Helix
A helix is the locus of a point moving along and around a cylinder, the two movements being in a constant ratio.

Helices are either right-hand (clockwise) or left-hand (anti-clockwise) and are important in engineering because of their use in the design of screws and springs. Another example is the lead screw on a lathe and the curve generated when turning between centres.

Helices are either drawn as a single line or as part of a screw thread. The student must remember that the lead (or pitch) is the distance between the 'peaks' of each successive revolution, and that this distance between the top of each turn is divided into the same number of divisions as the end elevation circle (at least eight).

Archimedean spiral
An Archimedean spiral is the locus of a point whose movement radially is uniform to its angular movement.
(An example of an Archimedean spiral is the groove on a gramophone record.)

In order to draw an Archimedean spiral the outer circle diameter is required. This may be worded as 'the spiral travels to a maximum of 100 mm'; in effect, the spiral is within a circle of 100 mm diameter. The spiral does not start (or finish) at the centre of such a circle. It may well start some distance away from the centre. However, having established its starting and finishing points it is then necessary to plot the number of convolutions or revolutions required.

Involute

An involute is the locus traced by a point on the end of a straight line as that line unwinds from the circumference of a circle, without slipping.

An involute is rather like someone wrapping or unwrapping a piece of string around a cotton-reel. The piece of string must be kept under tension. The finger and thumb holding the end of the string will trace a path.

Involutes are used in the design of gear teeth.

Chapter 10   Lines and laminae

A line suspended in space between horizontal and vertical planes can be projected onto those planes orthographically. However, the only time that the line can be measured for its **true length** will be when the line is **parallel** to one of the **planes of projection.** In all other instances the line will appear foreshortened. If the line is not parallel to any plane then it must be made so in order to ascertain its true length.

Students seem to experience some difficulty in understanding questions on lines and laminae in space. Whether the question is about a single line or about the three lines that make up the lamina, the **basic** question is really about true lengths. If the student will accept the fact that the only time anything can be measured for its true length is when it is parallel to some reference plane, then it is towards that fact that the student must work.

Lines or laminae in space, like any other orthographic projection, **must be projected** from one view to another. Any alteration or movement in one view must automatically affect the position of the object in the other two views. It often helps to use a ruler or pencil in the case of a simple line and a set-square, in the case of lamina, to 'work out' a simulated problem. Using a large piece of paper made up into a 3-dimensional mock room and with the aid of your pencil or set-square, try and emulate the problem set. In effect, your 'paper room' acts as the planes of reference and by moving your pencil or set-square it is much easier to visualise each movement that you will have to plot and project.

Laminae present a rather more difficult projection but I have found that if students treat them as **three separate lines** whenever possible then the problem is considerably lessened.

Another useful guide is that students, if possible, should start with the plan and project up to the front elevation.

It is well worth spending time learning to be successful with this particular aspect of geometry as questions on this topic occur frequently in examination papers.

Chapter 11   Orthographic projection

One cannot 'revise' orthographic projection as one would learn a mathematical proof or indeed in the same way that the previous chapters have been revised. The **only** way to improve and to retain the skill required in orthographic projection is to 'do'. By that I mean practice, practice, practice. The student cannot possibly hope to turn up to an examination and do well if he or she has neglected to draw at least two worthwhile drawings every week.

It is very evident from past experience that those students who fail to finish work set in lessons or those who very rarely present a homework, gradually fall behind in skill and the ability to 'get on' with a drawing efficiently and accurately. It becomes a vicious circle, the further they fall behind, the harder it is to present a decent drawing and so they fall even further behind.

Orthographic projection is the common language of the engineer and is about communication. If the drawing is incorrect then the communication is incorrect and a great deal of time and money can be lost.

Orthographic projection as it's name states is a **projection** and the examiner will be awarding marks to those students whom he can see have projected correctly, while he will penalise heavily those whose work obviously has little relationship within the views.

Establish and **state** your angle of **projection,** either 1st- or 3rd-angle and state the **scale.**

1st-angle projection is traditionally British and in this system the object is imagined as being suspended in space. The lines of projection are projected 'through' the object onto the relative plans of projection. In other words what you see in front of you appears on the 'wall' behind. The plan is below the front elevation and the side elevation can be to either side of the front elevation.

3rd-angle projection is used in the United States of America and on the Continent and will eventually become the national and international means of projection. In this system, the object is imagined as being suspended within a 'mirrored box' or transparent box. The impression is either 'reflected' back onto the plane of reference or the object recorded on the transparent plane of reference. The result is the same. The plan is above the front elevation and the side views are positioned either side of the front elevation.

Chapter 12   Auxiliary projection

In orthographic projection the object is viewed at right-angles from the front, the side and from above. These views are known as front elevation, side elevation and plan. However, it may be advantageous to view the object from a different angle other than at 90°. This may be for a variety of reasons: to obtain a clearer view of a particular aspect of the work or to obtain a true shape of a particular face or surface that has appeared foreshortened in the standard three orthographic views. Whatever the reason may be, these oblique views are known as **auxiliary** views.

There are two auxiliary views, namely auxiliary elevations and auxiliary plans.

An auxiliary elevation is obtained when the object is viewed obliquely from the **front** or **side.** The 'eye' is still **parallel** to the horizontal plane. Therefore, the **height** of the view will be the same as for the front elevation or side elevation. In order to obtain this auxiliary elevation the lines of projection are taken **from** the **plan** just as the front elevation was projected from its plan. The angle of auxiliary projection can be any angle but is usually 30°, 45° or 60°.

An auxiliary plan is obtained when the object is viewed obliquely from **above.** The 'eye' is still parallel to the vertical plane and therefore the **widths** do not alter in the auxiliary view.

The auxiliary plan is obtained by projecting from the front elevation onto the new groundlines, normally referred to as XY or X^1Y^1. As above, the angle of auxiliary is normally 30°, 45° or 60° to the horizontal.

When projecting these new lines from the orthographic views it is good practice to number or letter your individual lines as they are taken from the particular points of reference.

Chapter 13   Isometric/oblique projection

Isometric projection
Although orthographic projection is the 'main' language of the draughtsman, it is sometimes necessary to be able to 'explain' or communicate to a wider or less knowledgeable group of people. In order to make certain views absolutely clear and therefore easier to understand pictorial views are used. **Isometric projection** is one such pictorial view.

Isometric projection uses vertical lines and lines at 30° to the horizontal. It is upon these isometric lines that the pictorial image is built. Any measurements that are to be transferred from the orthographic must only be measured upon these isometric lines. It is impossible to transfer angles or measurements upon angular surfaces.

A difficult factor to overcome in pictorial projection is the planning or positioning of the object in relation to the paper. Another problem is the positioning of certain parts of the object in relation to other parts of the object as presented pictorially. Both these difficulties can be overcome by taking the maximum height, width and length of the object and placing this rectangle (or what have you!) into an isometric block. The student can then easily position this block on the paper and also know that the actual object must 'fit' within the limits of this block.

If the component is an awkward shape then a **series** of isometric blocks can be placed together to give the framework within which to work.

Most components have some circular part or parts and while this is relatively easy to draw orthographically it becomes rather more of a problem isometrically. The student must therefore be able to produce circles in isometric by either the **ordinate method** or by the **approximate arc method.**

Reference is often made to **isometric scale** on examination papers but in a negative fashion, i.e., 'do not draw to an isometric scale'. Therefore the student need not concern himself at this stage with this particular aspect of isometric projection.

Oblique projection
In oblique, one face of the object is presented at right-angles to the views—in fact it looks exactly the same as any orthographic view might look. However all other faces are inclined at 45° (in some instances this can be 30° or 60°). The front face view will be seen as full size but **all** measurements along the 45° axes are **half** the scale size. If the student draws these lines full size it will be clear that the figure appears out-of-proportion. Remember that pictorial views are views in communication and that measurements are not generally taken **from** them. They are really to give the orthographic projection more visual 'back-up'.

The drawing of circles in oblique can only be produced by the ordinate method. While the vertical lines remain full size the 45° axis must be halved. It is therefore very much more sensible to draw any circles in the front plane and to this extent oblique has an advantage over isometric.

Chapter 14   Sections of solids

All the views that have been discussed so far have dealt with outside views. Sometimes it is necessary to gain an insight into the internal workings or configuration of a component. In order to do so **sections** are taken through various views and 'exposed'. It is rather like cutting, if that were possible, the object in half with a large knife. Those surfaces that are actually **cut** with the knife are **cross-hatched** with lines at 45°.

Remember that if an object is cut at a place that contains a hole, the back curve of the hole is untouched by the cut and is therefore **not** hatched.

This 'knife' cut is known as the **cutting plane.**

Chapter 15   Intersections

Intersections or interpenetrations occur when two solid geo-metric shapes meet. They appear joined to one another and where they join form a **curve** or **line of interpenetration.** It is important to be able to plot this line accurately because the surfaces of the two shapes may have to be shown later as a development.

The best way to deal with intersections, which can be varied and complex, is to try and visualise planes or 'slices' taken through the object. The more 'slices' taken the more accurately can the curve or line be plotted.

The intersection of a right circular cone at right-angles with a cylindrical pipe serves as an example. As the various cuts are taken through the cone and pipe the circles that make up the cone will either become smaller or larger, while the slices through the pipe get narrower or wider. Each cut must be exam-ined and the points of contact (or intersection) marked. These contact points are then projected around the orthographic views.

At least eight cutting sections are needed to produce an accurate result. Do not attempt to draw masses of cuts in the front elevation and then project them all around at the same time. Take each section one at a time and **complete** its plotting before attempting to deal with the second section.

Remember that if a straight-sided object, like for example, a hexagonal prism, intersects another straight-sided object, the resulting interpenetration line will be straight-lined. If however a curved figure intersects any other type of figure, the result in general will be a curve of interpenetration.

Chapter 16   Developments

Developments are the 'flattening-out' of objects onto sheet material, in the most economical way possible, so that they may be cut and fashioned and shaped into the required design.

These developments could also be termed as **patterns** or **templates.**

In order to be able to make the object accurately it is necessary to calculate its shape by the development of a three-dimensional component onto a two-dimensional material. Once this development or template is drawn, many copies can be produced of an identical nature. Inaccuracy or badly drawn developments can cost the manufacturer dearly.

Developments are essentially of two types—**parallel development** and **radial development.**

Parallel development

This method is used for developing those shapes or objects that have parallel sides or a uniform cross-section. It would therefore be used for prisms and cylinders.

In setting out parallel development the plan of the object is drawn in order to calculate not only the length of the circumference but also to position the **generators** for plotting purposes.

The numbering or lettering of each generator on the plan, the elevations and the development area is critical. The student will face an impossible task if these numbers or letters do not correspond or co-ordinate. The initial positioning of the numbers will also affect the final shape of the development. This can be most important when working out economical cutting from sheet material or the joining of short or long seams.

Radial line development

This method of development is used for objects that have a vertex (or apex) and a base, namely cones and pyramids. The actual shape to be developed may not have an apex but side lines extended would eventually join at an apex. (For example a frustum of a cone.)

The set-up is very similar to that of the parallel development in that it is necessary to draw the plan, in order to calculate the length of the circumference and the generators for plotting points. Careful numbering is essential.

The most marked difference between the two types of development is that in the parallel development all the lines seen are true lengths. In radial line development the only true lines will be those generators that make up the outside shape of the object itself. For example, a cone in elevation has true lengths from apex to the extreme positions of its base. (In fact, the outside lines that make up the cone shape.) Any other line that appears from the base line to the apex in the elevation is foreshortened.

The problem then is to transfer any point of reference on these foreshortened generators to the outside line where they will be seen as true line reference points.

All developments are stated as such, e.g., 'development of surface A', and they are cross-hatched at 45°.

Chapter 17   Layout and presentation

Information regarding layout and presentation will figure in the section on Examination Hints because the general impression that an examiner gains from his initial look at the work is extremely important.

However, the student can certainly 'revise' this aspect of the work by practising in spare moments the positioning of any orthographic drawings in relation to the paper to be drawn on. Students spend far too much time working out exactly, to the last millimetre, the position of the three orthographic views. It is something that has to be calculated as quickly as possible yet still achieving the correct 'balance'.

It is also good practice to make very quickly a pictorial sketch of what you think the orthographic views represent. This prevents drawing 'blind' and gives the student a base on which to work.

Printing is an aspect of the work that tends to be neglected and when the examination arrives it is surprising how difficult it is to suddenly become a good, neat printer. Style and expertise are only achieved as the result of practice.

Chapter 18   Sectioning

Whenever a component or object has been cut by a 'cutting plane', the cut surface is cross-hatched. However, it may well be that this component is made up of more than one piece or that in its manufacture different materials have been used. It is clear that certain 'rules' have to be made and these must be learnt.

The following items are **never** cross-hatched because even in a section they are shown as complete or whole items.

- (a) **Nuts and bolts**
- (b) **Studs**
- (c) **Keys** (in key ways)
- (d) **Gear teeth**
- (e) **Pins** (e.g. cotter)
- (f) **Screws**
- (g) **Ball bearings and ball races**
- (h) **Roller bearings and roller races**

Webs and **shafts** have rather a mixed convention.

If a web or shaft is cut parallel to its long axis (or longitudinally) then it is **NOT** cross-hatched. If the web or shaft is cut across its shortest axis (or laterally) then it **IS** cross-hatched.

All hatched lines are at 45° and if possible never more than 4 mm apart.

If two pieces of material are joined together then a cross-section would result in the hatching going different ways.

If two or more pieces of **different** materials are used then it must be made obvious, by alternating cross-hatching, that this is so.

As a good rule look at your cross-hatched section. If a straight line is within the cross-hatching and the hatching is all in the same direction as if it were one piece of material, then something is wrong. Either the straight line should not be there or you have two pieces of material and your hatching is incorrect.

Half-section
Applies to components that are symmetrical. It is considered unnecessary to show a complete section view. It is useful also because on the one view you have an external and an internal view.

Section in two planes
When it is necessary to section a component along two cutting planes, because one cutting plane will not give enough detail, a convention of 'two planes' is used. The resulting sectional view has no evidence of the two planes but the elevations will clearly show the cranked cutting line.

Aligned section
Used when features lie on a radial line that deviates from the main cutting plane. It makes the sectional view much easier.

Chapter 19   Useful data

The draughtsman is the middle man between designer and workman and it is his/her job to make sure that the workman understands fully what is required. As a result, certain standards, conventions or rules have evolved and all draughtsmen use this language so that no matter where the drawings are 'read', they can clearly be understood.

Abbreviations
Rather than having to write out every word or phrase to express what is required a whole list of abbreviations have become standardised. The student should know these as they may well appear on examination papers.

Nuts and bolts
This data is perhaps the most widely used of all. Nearly every examination drawing paper makes some reference to, or requires the drawing of, a nut and bolt. There is not much to learn but it is well worth spending time on making sure that you know not only how to draw a nut and bolt but also in what proportion they should appear.

The key to success lies in memorising a few simple formulae.

All the measurements are based on D. D is the diameter of the bolt and will be shown on the drawing paper as, for example, M12 or M8. The M stands for metric and is of no consequence when actually drawing the bolt.

Basic formulae (for a nominal nut and bolt)
Bolt

Distance across flats of hexagonal head	$= 1.5D$
Distance across corners of hexagonal head	$= 1.75D$
Head height	$= 0.7D$

Nut

Distance across flats of hexagonal nut	$= 1.5D$
Distance across corners of hexagonal nut	$= 1.75D$
Thickness of nut	$= 0.8D$
Locking nut thickness	$= 0.5D$

Washer
Internal diameter $= D + 0.5$ mm up to M10 bolts
$\qquad\qquad\quad = D + 1.0$ mm over M10 bolts

Length of thread

Bolts up to and including 125 mm	$= 2D + 6$ mm
Over 125 mm and up to 200 mm	$= 2D + 12$ mm
Over 200 mm	$= 2D + 25$ mm

Screw threads
The student should learn the profiles of the various screw threads that are in general use.

(a) **Whitworth**
   British Standard Engineering form. Fairly coarse thread.
   British Standard Fine is similar but closer pitch.
(b) **British Association thread (BA)**
   A millimetre thread used for instrument and electrical work.
   Sizes 0 BA to 25 BA.
(c) **American Sellers thread**
   Basic American thread made in both coarse and fine forms.
(d) **Unified thread**
   The Unified thread has been accepted by North America and Britain in both coarse and fine form. Three classes of fit are allowed: 1A, 2A, 3A, external thread ordinary, good class, and precision work respectively. 1B, 2B, 3B, denote internal threads of similar standard. An instruction could read:

¾ 12 UNF 2A to indicate a ¾″ dia., twelve threads per inch, good class Unified external thread.

(e) **Square threads**
Used for threads mostly in machines which have to take continuous pressure movement in both clockwise and anti-clockwise direction. Machine slides are often operated by square thread screw threads.

(f) **Acme threads**
Chiefly used for lead screws on lathes.

(g) **Buttress threads**
Used where the pressure is chiefly in one direction, as in quick release vices and slides: a half nut disengages on the return.

(h) **Metric thread**
A 60° angle thread similar to American Sellers thread, sizes in millimetres. Fine and coarse forms. Instruction could read: M6 × 0.75, which would indicate a metric thread 6 mm in dia. with a pitch of ¾ mm.

Fastenings—rivets
(a) **Snaphead** Standard type for ordinary work
(b) **Panhead** Second form of head for normal work
(c) **Countersunk/cone** Flush finish on surface–conical head
(d) **Raised and countersunk** Flat special heads where small projection is required
(e) **Panhead/tapered neck** Taper gives better compression of the plates

Fastenings—setscrews
(a) **Countersunk**
(b) **Square**
(c) **Cheese**
(d) **Roundhead**
(e) **Raised**
(f) **Grub**

All types are used frequently and especially for light work. Grub screws may have square heads, cross-slotted heads or a sunk hexagon for tightening. Self-tapping screws are now used more often for fastening thin metal sheet especially in the motor industry.

Conventions
Conventions are used because many engineering details are difficult and tedious to draw. Imagine how long it would take to draw

a screw thread in detail. There are many conventions in engineering and the examples shown in the relevant chapter are the most common that the student is likely to encounter:

(a) **Breaklines**
(b) **Knurling**
(c) **Square on sharp**
(d) **Springs**
(e) **Holes on circular pitch**
(f) **Holes on linear pitch**
(g) **External threads**
(h) **Internal threads**

Quick revision test

On the next five pages the student can set himself a series of very quick and simple tests to act as a useful revision exercise. Cover up the answer page and spend five to ten minutes in a spare moment making absolutely sure that the basic groundwork is well known.

If the answer to any question is yes, then how would you set about constructing or drawing that answer.

If the answer is no, then what is the positive answer to the question.

In other words use the test to **stimulate** thought and to provoke alternative questions and answers.

Key test one

Questions	Yes	No
1 Does a bisector cut a line and an angle in half?		
2 Is an acute angle more than 90°?		
3 Is a reflex angle greater than 180°?		
4 Does 1 to 12 in a scale mean 1/12th full size?		
5 Is the outside of a circle called the perimeter?		
6 The apex is the top of a triangle.		
7 The hypotenuse is the side adjacent to a right-angle.		
8 A rhombus has all four sides equal in length.		
9 A trapezium has all four sides parallel.		
10 A hexagon is a five-sided figure.		
11 The angle subtended at the centre of a circle is $360/n$.		
12 A circumscribing circle is found by bisecting the angles of a triangle.		
13 A triangle drawn within a semi-circle with its base as diameter is a right-angled triangle.		
14 Parallelograms have opposite sides equal.		
15 The bisector of two chords is the centre of that circle.		
16 Complementary angles add up to more than 90°.		
17 A scale of 1 mm to 1 m means that every metre on the ground is represented by 1 mm on the paper.		
18 A diagonal scale can be read even down to 0.01 of a mm.		
19 If the angles of a triangle are equal then the sides are also equal.		
20 The angles of a rhomboid add up to less than 360°.		

Answer page 222   √ = Yes   X = No

Key test two

Questions	Yes	No
1 The centre of a polygon is found by bisecting the interior angles.		
2 Triangles with the same base length and the same vertical height are equal in area.		
3 A normal is the perpendicular to a tangent.		
4 The internal tangent to two circles is found by the difference of the radii of the two circles.		
5 A locus is the path traced by a point.		
6 A trunnion cannot move from its position.		
7 A slider is a pivot which moves along a fixed straight line.		
8 A circle touching an acute angle will have the bisector of that angle passing through its centre.		
9 If three points are joined and the lines joining them are bisected, the bisector will be the centre of a circle touching the three points.		
10 Similar figures have equal areas.		
11 When the height alone of a triangle is halved its area is halved.		
12 If a circle touches a given point its centre must lie in a line drawn through the point and the centre of the given circle.		
13 If the sides of a square are halved its area is halved.		
14 The locus of a pendulum in relation to the clock is a straight line.		
15 The area of a parallelogram is the base multiplied by the vertical height.		
16 A triangle is equal in area to a rectangle with the triangle's base and half its vertical height.		
17 A tangent is a straight line touching a circle but not cutting it.		
18 The direct common tangent is known also as the internal tangent.		
19 Similar figures can be constructed using radiating lines.		
20 The angles of a regular polygon are 72°.		

Answer page 222   √ = Yes   X = No

Key test three

Questions	Yes	No
1 A helix is the locus of a point moving around a cylinder without slipping		
2 A lead is the distance between one complete revolution.		
3 The epicycloid is the locus of a point on the circumference of a circle that rolls along a straight line without slipping.		
4 The Archimedean spiral is the locus of a point whose movement radially is proportional to its angular movement.		
5 An ellipse can be treated as a locus.		
6 An ellipse is formed when a cylinder or a cone is cut by an inclined plane.		
7 An ellipse can be drawn by a compass method.		
8 The parabola is the locus of a point in a constant ratio of greater than one to a fixed line and a fixed point.		
9 A trammel can be used to draw a hyperbola.		
10 The minor axis is half the major axis in an ellipse.		
11 Asymptotes are lines that continually approach nearer to some curve without ever reaching it.		
12 In the parabola the vertex is equi-distant from the directrix and the focus.		
13 It is impossible to construct a tangent to an ellipse.		
14 The directrix is perpendicular to the line of symmetry passing through the focus.		
15 The pedal of a moving bicycle traces a cycloid in relation to the ground.		
16 Helices occur in screw threads and springs.		
17 The tightness of a spring is governed by the lead.		
18 In the hyperbola the vertex will be positioned between the directrix and focus in the constant ratio of the problem.		
19 Lines from the focal points of an ellipse to a point on the ellipse will be equal.		
20 The length of overturn of an involute to a circle equals its circumference.		

Answer page 222   √ = Yes   X = No

Key test four

Questions	Yes	No
1 Can a true length only be measured when it is parallel to a plane?		
2 First-angle is an American projection.		
3 In first-angle, lines are projected 'through' the object.		
4 An end elevation can be drawn on either side of a front elevation.		
5 The front elevation is placed on the E.V.P.		
6 In order to obtain an auxiliary view extra projecting planes are needed.		
7 An auxiliary plan is obtained when the viewer views the object parallel to the horizontal.		
8 In the auxiliary plan all lines projected will appear foreshortened except the widths and any line or face at right-angles to the viewer.		
9 Isometric is 45° axes to the horizontal.		
10 An oblique projection can be at 30°, 45°, 60° to the right-face.		
11 All lines on the isometric axes are halved.		
12 It is possible to draw isometric and oblique circles by the co-ordinate method.		
13 The plan of a line in space is swung parallel to the V.P. – it will appear as a true length in the front elevation.		
14 Measurements can only be made on the verticals and isometric axes in isometric projections.		
15 The thickness of laminae must be taken into account when solving the problem.		
16 Isometric scale is used to obtain greater visual accuracy.		
17 Oblique is rather more widely used than isometric.		
18 It is advisable to encase all pictorial views in a box that will allow for correct positioning.		
19 There are correct and incorrect ways of viewing an object in oblique.		
20 Any angles on an orthographic projection can be transferred to an isometric projection.		

Answer page 222   √ = Yes   X = No

Key test five

Questions	Yes	No
1 Cross-hatching lines are 60° to the horizontal.		
2 When a section has two cutting planes the orthographic view shows it as one plane.		
3 Developments are used in sheet-metalwork.		
4 When two solids meet, the line of meeting is called an interpenetration.		
5 There is a standard book of conventions for engineering students.		
6 Internal and external threads are shown as the same.		
7 There are two main methods of developments.		
8 Radial line development is used on solids of uniform section.		
9 It is impossible to cross-hatch different materials or components that lie next to one another.		
10 Webs cut longitudinally are not cross-hatched.		
11 Webs cut transversely are cross-hatched.		
12 Developments are used to economise on materials and to obtain as many pressings as possible.		
13 Two pipes of equal diameter meet at right-angles to one another – the intersection will be a straight line.		
14 The distance across the flats of a hexagonal nut is 1.75D.		
15 The nut of a hexagonal bolt is thicker than the bolt head.		
16 The end view of a screw thread can be shown by two circles.		
17 Webs are necessary in engineering for support and to reduce weight in a component.		
18 A hole cut longitudinally will appear as two parallel lines.		
19 Sections are necessary because many components have complex internal details.		
20 All measurements for the drawing of a bolt are based upon the outside diameter of the bolt.		

Answer page 222   √ = Yes X = No

Key test answers

Questions	Key test 1 Yes	No	Key test 2 Yes	No	Key test 3 Yes	No	Key test 4 Yes	No	Key test 5 Yes	No
1	√		√			X	√			X
2		X	√		√			X	√	
3	√		√			X	√		√	
4	√			X	√		√		√	
5		X		X	√			X	√	
6	√			X	√		√			X
7		X	√		√			X	√	
8	√		√			X	√			X
9		X	√			X		X		X
10		X		X		X	√		√	
11	√		√		√			X	√	
12		X	√		√		√		√	
13	√			X		X	√			X
14	√			X	√		√			X
15	√		√			X		X	√	
16		X	√		√		√		√	
17		X	√		√			X	√	
18	√			X	√		√		√	
19	√		√			X	√		√	
20		X	√		√			X	√	